Practice For a Purpose

Practice For a Purpose

Writing Activities for Classroom, Lab, and Self-Study

Muriel Harris

Purdue University

Houghton Mifflin Company   Boston

Dallas   Geneva, Illinois   Hopewell, New Jersey   Palo Alto

Printed in the U.S.A.

ISBN: 0-395-34248-1

ABCDEFGHIJ-A-89876543

Acknowledgment is made to the following authors and publishers for permission to quote from their works:

William Allman, from "Twisting Slowly in the Wind," *Science 83*, June 1983. Reprinted by permission. Ammirati and Purvis, Inc., New York, BMW advertisement. By permission. Timothy Bannon, from "The Board Game," copyright © 1982 by *Harper's* Magazine. All rights reserved. Reprinted from the December 1982 issue by special permission. David Burnham, from "How Long Should the Arm of the Law Be?" and "The Silent Power of the N.S.A." © 1982/1983 by the New York Times Company. Reprinted by permission. Fox Butterfield, from "The New Vietnam Scholarship," © 1982 by the New York Times Company. Reprinted by permission. Stephen Budiansky, from "How Does Smoke Kill?" *Science 83*, May 1983. Reprinted by permission. William Bennett and Joel Gurin, from "Do Diets Really Work? *Science 82*, March 1982. Reprinted by permission. Robert Christopher, from "Changing Face of Japan," © 1983 by The New York Times Company. Reprinted by permission. Christopher Connell, "New on the School Curriculum: War 101," from the July 10, 1983, *Lafayette Journal and Courier*. Reprinted by permission. Richard Critchfield, excerpted from "Science and the Villager: The Last Sleeper Wakes." Excerpted by permission of *Foreign Affairs*, Fall 1982. Copyright 1982 by the Council on Foreign Relations, Inc. Gary Deeb, from "Finale: A misMASH of Poor Acting, Bad Drama," from the March 4, 1983, *Lafayette Journal and Courier*. Reprinted by permission. "The Decade that Failed" © 1982 by The New York Times Company. Reprinted by permission. Richard Freedman, from "The War of the Falkland Islands." Excerpted by permission of *Foreign Affairs*, Fall 1982. Copyright 1982 by the Council on Foreign Relations, Inc. Vivian Gornick, from "A Ride on the New York Subway," *Village Voice*, December 21, 1972. Reprinted by permission. Thomas Griffin, "Where Do You Get Your News?" *Time*, December 6, 1982. Copyright © 1982 by Time Inc. All rights reserved. Reprinted by permission from *Time*. "Hot Tub-itis" *Science 83*, January/February 1983. Reprinted by permission. Christopher Hitchens, from "Minority Report," *The Nation*, May 14, 1983. Copyright 1983 The Nation Magazine, The Nation Associates. Inc. David Jones, from "What's Wrong with Our Defense Establishment," © 1982 by The New York Times Company. Reprinted by permission. Alfred Kazin, from *A Walker in the City*, copyright 1951, 1979 by Alfred Kazin. Reprinted by permission of Harcourt Brace Jovanovich. Robert Kraus, from "Hot Airbags" copyright © 1982 by *Harper's* Magazine. All rights reserved. Reprinted from the December 1982 issue by special permission. Jane Lazarre, from "Growing Up Red: Remembering a Communist Childhood in New York." Reprinted courtesy *Village Voice*. Fran Lebowitz, from "Good Weather and its Propensity to Frequent the Better Neighborhoods." In *Metropolitan Life* by Fran Lebowitz. © 1978 E.P. Dutton. By permission. Fran Lebowitz, from

Contents

To the Student

When I was a student I used to wonder why authors felt the need to write introductions to their books. If they had done their jobs well, I thought, their books should speak for themselves. Having written this book, however, I find that an introduction is actually useful because it provides the best means to tell you about what you will find in the following pages. Also, I want to introduce you to the purpose of this book and to a few approaches—some of which may be new to you—that you will find here.

First, a word about the question of purpose—that is, what this book is trying to accomplish. Writing, like any other worthwhile skill, requires considerable practice. You will find here pages and pages of exercises to keep you writing, because that's the way (or, as some people say, the only way) to learn to write well. Write every day if you can, write in every composition class meeting, write every time you work in your writing lab or center. Just keep writing. This collection of "finger exercises" is meant to keep you writing, thinking about writing, and reading other people's writing.

Now, let's consider a few approaches that may not be familiar. First, you won't always be working alone. Second, you really will be practicing, much as you do in practice sessions before a big game or a concert or a performance. Third, you'll find some examples of writing in this book that are good, some that are acceptable, and some that are real disasters. Let's look at these one at a time.

WORKING IN GROUPS

First, the matter of not working alone all the time. This book offers you some opportunities to work with other writers. Certain exercises suggest that you form a small group with several other writers to discuss, brainstorm, or plan. While some of your thinking needs to be done privately, you also need to learn how to contribute and work effectively in groups, a skill you will need on the job and in any situation when you work with other people. Also, as you will notice when you are in a group, sometimes ideas flow better when several people are contributing—in fact, sometimes you even think better and more productively as you hear other people's ideas and react to them. People in the business world know this fact and make use of it in "think tanks," organizations in which people do intensive research or problem-solving together. The idea is simply to put some people together and let the sparks fly. Often, better sparks (even bonfires) are the result.

As a writer, you have another reason for working in groups: you need to hear how your audience reacts to your writing. Thus, other exercises in this book ask you to form groups in order to read and offer comments on one another's writing. These small groups are meant as help sessions and should encourage open, honest exchanges of suggestions and recommendations that will help you improve your own writing and become a better reader of other people's writing. Working in small evaluation groups can be a valuable experience, but it can also be merely wasted time if you decide not to be honest. For example, you may read another writer's paper and discover some weak spots, but because you don't want to offend the person you may offer a "Yeah, it's a pretty good paper" type of comment. When that happens, there are two losers. The other person has lost a chance to learn how to make his or her writing better, and you have lost a chance to learn how to put into words what the writing needed. Of course, you may also lose a friend if the other person hands in the paper and gets a depressingly low grade. You weren't there to help as a friend should.

For these reasons, then, you should take advantage of those exercises that ask you to form a small group with several other writers. If possible, try to limit your group to three or four people. A group this size is large enough to get a variety of responses and small enough for everyone to be actively involved. Some of the exercises will require writing in one another's books, some will suggest that you spend the time discussing or planning, and some will ask you to evaluate one another's writing or a sample of writing included in the book. All members of the group should try to keep it moving forward, realizing that a bit of socializing is part of the fun of group dynamics but that there is important work to be done.

TAKING ADVANTAGE OF PRACTICE

The second aspect of this book that may need some explaining is that it is not a textbook but a practice book. There are no lengthy explanations of how to write, only suggestions for writing practice. Practice—and lots of it—goes into the making of good tennis players, good violinists, good actors, good football players, or good photographers. Knowing that, you really don't need to be convinced of the value of practice, as long as you recognize that it's only practice and not the Big Game. In the game—or concert or whatever—you are on display and are graded or evaluated on your performance. But not in the practice sessions. Practice sessions are for flexing some muscles, trying some new approaches, pushing yourself a little farther—just to see if you can do it. In that way, this book offers you all kinds of practice before the Big Game when you hand in writing to be evaluated. You may not have encountered this approach before, but it is the purpose of this book, and it can help you a great deal. You won't be practicing grammar here (correcting commas, undangling dangling modifiers, piecing together fragments); instead, you will be practicing the more complex aspects of writing, the rhetorical skills and the thinking skills.

As you have probably noticed, writing is a rather complicated act; some people think it's not unlike playing a one-man band. Just as the player stomps on a drum with his foot, rings bells with one hand while bowing a violin, strums a guitar with the other hand, and simultaneously blows on a harmonica, you the writer have to juggle all kinds of constraints as you think of what you want to say, how to say it, what words to use, and where to put the commas. Moreover, you are told to be clear, to be organized, to consider your audience, to choose the right words, to eliminate wordiness, to keep your subjects in agreement with your verbs, and, by the way, to spell everything correctly.

Thus, it isn't surprising that when you're learning how to improve your writing, you simply can't attend to everything at once. For that reason *Practice For a Purpose* offers you the opportunity to try just a few things at a time. In the first chapter there are exercises to help you understand something about the composing process, how writers write. In the second chapter you'll have some opportunities to practice different types of planning strategies. Another chapter focuses on planning for large-scale revision, in other chapters you'll look more closely at paragraphs, sentences, words, and so on. Bit by bit, as you progress through this book, you have opportunities to concentrate your energies on just a few skills at a time. Just as you spend some time practicing your serve in tennis, and then your forehand, and then your backhand, before you actually play a game, so too in this book you'll be practicing many skills, one at a time. But do remember that these are practice sessions. Remember, too, that the best practice sessions are those where you take some risks, try some new approaches, and expect some of your attempts to fall flat. That's a natural part of the process of getting better at something.

You may find, in using this book, that you need more space in which to plan or write out your responses to the exercises. It's difficult to know how much room to leave on the page, since writers invariably differ in their approaches to answering questions: some write at length, others are more concise. For that reason, if you find that you need additional space, you should probably complete some of the longer exercises on separate sheets of paper. Just be sure you keep them all together; you may also want to annotate your book to indicate that certain exercises were handled in this manner.

EVALUATING WRITING

And now a word about the third point I mentioned at the beginning of this introduction. This practice book contains some writing that is good, some that is ordinary, everyday kind of prose, some that's not so bad but could stand some improvements, and some that is really just plain bad writing. There are people who say that you should expose yourself only to good writing, but there are others who think that you can learn to recognize good writing better if you can compare it to bad writing. One teacher of writing put it succinctly when, in defense of the bad example, he pointed to the difficulty of knowing what "wet" is if you live in a desert. Sometimes, you simply aren't able to appreciate what good is until you are confronted with a bad example. So don't be surprised by the uneven quality of the excerpts in this book. Instead, see how much you can sharpen your critical skills by learning to recognize bad writing and learning how to make it better. Then you will be able to spot weaknesses in your own writing and improve them.

Finally, I would like to thank the many students whom I've worked with in classes and in our writing lab at Purdue who volunteered to let their writing be included here for you to read. And thanks also to some excellent teachers of writing, Jacob Adler, Leonora Woodman, and Judith Kilborn, who first helped their students to learn to write well and then offered to share their students' writing with you.

I hope you enjoy using this book, and I invite you to let me know how you like it. Did it help you become a better writer? How did you use the book? What exercises should be changed? Do you have any pieces of writing that you would like to offer as future samples? I enjoy putting words on paper and reading other people's words on paper, so I look forward to hearing from you.

Muriel Harris
The Writing Lab
Purdue University

Practice For a Purpose

1
The Writing Process

GETTING ACQUAINTED WITH THE WRITING PROCESS

Exercise 1

One way to learn more about the writing process and about differences and similarities of writing processes among people is to interview some experienced writers. Select two people who write frequently. You might try local journalists, teachers at your institution, people in nearby businesses who frequently write reports and memos, and administrative staff at your college or university who often need to write as part of their work. Ask these people the following questions:

1. How often and how much does the person write?

    a. _____

    _____

    b. _____

    _____

2. What kinds of writing does the person do?

    a. _____

    _____

    b. _____

    _____

3. How long does it take the person to complete the writing in an adequate or satisfactory manner?

1

a. _____

_____

b. _____

_____

4. What do the writers do when they get stuck? Do they generally have some confidence that, despite the temporary problem, they will eventually push through and complete the task?

a. _____

_____

b. _____

_____

5. Can the writers describe the various steps they follow as they write?

a. _____

_____

b. _____

_____

6. How much time do they spend revising?

a. _____

_____

b. _____

_____

7. What are a few of the basic principles that guide these writers as they write?

a. _____

_____

b. _____

_____

What are some of the similarities and differences between the two writers you interviewed?

Similarities: _____

_____

_____

Differences: _____

_____

_____

Exercise 2

Another way to learn about the writing process is to interview people skilled in other areas and to compare their procedures with those of a writer. Select two people who are skilled in other areas, such as a competent athlete, an artist, a musician, an actor, or another person who has developed a performing skill. Ask these two people the following questions:

1. Are they nervous when they have to perform or to play before a group, in a competition, or in a test situation? If so, what do they do to calm themselves?

   a. _____

   _____

   b. _____

   _____

2. If they occasionally perform less than adequately, how does this affect their next performance? Does recalling past successes help?

   a. _____

   _____

b. _____

_____

3. What steps do they go through as they perform? Do they plan or rehearse anything mentally? Do they keep reminding themselves of what to do?

a. _____

_____

b. _____

_____

4. What are a few of the basic principles that guide them as they perform?

a. _____

_____

b. _____

_____

What are some of the similarities and differences between these skilled performers and the experienced writer?

Similarities: _____

_____

_____

Differences: _____

_____

_____

Exercise 3

Another way to learn about your own writing processes is to describe them. Answer the following questions and then write a description of your habits and processes.

1. Writing habits

    a. What kind of place do you prefer when you write? _____

    _____

    b. At what time of day or night do you prefer to write? _____

    _____

    c. How long do you usually write at one session? _____

    _____

    d. If you take a break, what do you do during your break? _____

    _____

    e. Do you prefer to write in silence or with noise around you? _____

    What kind of noise? _____

    _____

    f. What kind of pen, pencil, typewriter, or word processor do you use?

    _____

    g. What other special requirements do you have for writing? _____

    _____

    _____

2. Writing processes

    a. How detailed are your plans? _____
    b. Do you begin with a vague notion of what you want to say or a more

    detailed sense of what you want to write about? _____

    _____

c. Do your plans generally tend to change as you write? _____

_____

d. Do you discover new things you want to say as you write? _____

_____

e. Does this discovery continue all the way through your writing or

does it generally occur near the beginning or the end? _____

_____

f. Do you make outlines? _____ If so, when? _____

_____

g. Do you generally find that you need more material as you write?

_____

If so, what do you do? _____

_____

h. Do you make many changes and revise as you progress, or do you

prefer to revise after you have finished a draft? _____

_____

GUIDELINES FOR THE WRITING PROCESS

Subject

Exercise 1

We write about some subjects we already know about and some that we learn about. By answering the following questions, you can create a profile of subjects that you know about.

1. When I was in elementary school, I lived in _____

The things I remember most vividly about that place were _____

_____

_____

What I disliked most intensely about that place was _____

_____

_____

2. In elementary school, I was most likely to do the following after

school: _____

_____

In high school, I spent my time doing the following: _____

_____

3. The holidays celebrated in our home or community were: _____

_____

_____

What I remember most about those celebrations: _____

_____

_____

4. The clubs I belonged to were _____

_____

5. The most interesting thing about my family is _____

_____

6. In high school I worried most about _____

_____

7. The subject I enjoyed most in high school was _____

_____ because _____

_____

8. Some sports and hobbies that interest me are _____

_____

_____

9. I've spent some summers doing the following: _____

_____

_____

10. I've traveled to _____

_____

11. Some magazines I like to read are _____

12. In a new town or city the first thing I want to know more about is

_____

_____

13. An organized group I belong to is _____

_____ . The special interest or purpose of that

group is _____

14. What I am proudest of about myself (or what I'd like other people to

know about me) is _____

_____

Exercise 2

To gather a profile of subjects you'd like to learn more about, try the following:

1. Find a topic index such as the one that appears in *Readers' Guide to Periodical Literature* or in your library's card catalog. Write down five topics that look potentially interesting.

   a. _____

   b. _____

   c. _____

   d. _____

   e. _____

2. Skim the headlines of a local newspaper or the table of contents of a magazine you like and write down five topics that look potentially interesting.

   a. _____

   b. _____

   c. _____

   d. _____

   e. _____

Exercise 3

Some subjects are interesting but not significant; others are significant but not particularly interesting to you. Rate the topics listed below on a scale of 1 to 3 as follows:

$$1 = \text{not very interesting or significant}$$
$$2 = \text{somewhat interesting or significant}$$
$$3 = \text{very interesting or significant}$$

After you have reacted to the listed topics, add five of your own but don't include your ratings. Confer with a small group of other writers and compare your ratings first for the group given here and then for the topics you added. Discuss the reasons for any differences in the ratings assigned by members of the group.

Topic	Interest level	Significance level
1. TV violence	____	____
2. Video games	____	____
3. Avalanches	____	____
4. Effects of computers on people	____	____
5. Abortion	____	____
6. "M.A.S.H."	____	____
7. Nuclear energy	____	____
8. Scientific predictions about the future appearance of the human race	____	____
9. Contemporary church problems	____	____
10. House plants	____	____
11. Chemical food additives	____	____
12. McDonald's vs. Wendy's	____	____
13. Soccer	____	____
14. Violence in South America	____	____
15. Ten Best Dressed Men list	____	____
16. _____	____	____
17. _____	____	____
18. _____	____	____

19. _____   ____   ____

20. _____   ____   ____

Describe the differences you found among members of your group and

some possible reasons for those differences: _____

_____

_____

_____

_____

Exercise 4

Listed below are some subjects of student papers. Using the same rating
scale as the previous exercise, rate these topics on their interest and significance. Form a small group with several other writers and compare your
responses.

Topic	Interest level	Significance level
1. The beauty of Niagara Falls	____	____
2. Reasons for students dropping out of college	____	____
3. Need for music education in the primary grades	____	____
4. Wildcat Creek being my favorite place to escape from the pressures of every-day life	____	____
5. The value of vocational education	____	____
6. A family vacation	____	____

7. Social, economic, and psychological
    adjustments after divorce   ____   ____

8. My dorm room as a reflection of my
    personality   ____   ____

9. The hazards of genetic engineering   ____   ____

10. Value of watching soaps on TV   ____   ____

11. Differences between TV news re-
     porting and newspaper coverage   ____   ____

12. Qualities of a good military officer   ____   ____

13. Changes in women's roles in movies
     from the 1950s to the 1980s   ____   ____

14. My grandmother   ____   ____

15. False advertising claims in popular
     ads   ____   ____

Exercise 5

Form a small group with several other writers and decide which of the
following topics seem manageable in a three- to four-page paper. If the
topic is not manageable, suggest a more limited topic on the line below.

	Topic	Manageable	Not manageable
1.	Getting to know people at this school	____	____
	_____		
	_____		
2.	How to windsurf	____	____
	_____		
	_____		

3. Reasons for teen-age alcoholism   ____   ____

_____

_____

4. The need for better teachers in American schools   ____   ____

_____

_____

5. Alternative energy sources   ____   ____

_____

_____

6. Problems of working mothers   ____   ____

_____

_____

7. Computer literacy   ____   ____

_____

_____

8. Advantages of catalog shopping   ____   ____

_____

_____

9. America's political relations with Mexico   ____   ____

_____

_____

10. Sexism in advertising   _____   _____

_____

_____

11. The Olympics and politics   _____   _____

_____

_____

Exercise 6

Select three of the broad, general subjects that you listed in Exercise 2 as ones that you'd like to learn more about, and formulate a topic that you could handle in three to four pages for each of these subjects.

1. _____

2. _____

3. _____

Some topics are so restricted that they can't be developed beyond a paragraph or two. Browse through a newspaper or magazine with very short items and find three examples of topics that are so restricted that nothing more can be added to the item you found.

1. _____

2. _____

3. _____

Audience

Exercise 1

List five topics for short papers that would be interesting to you but probably not to your teacher. Then list five topics that you think would be interesting to your teacher but that are not particularly interesting to you. Ask your teacher to agree or disagree with your selection of topics in section B.

A. Five topics that interest me but that probably don't interest my teacher:

1. _____

2. _____

3. _____

4. _____

5. _____

B. Five topics that I think my teacher would find interesting:

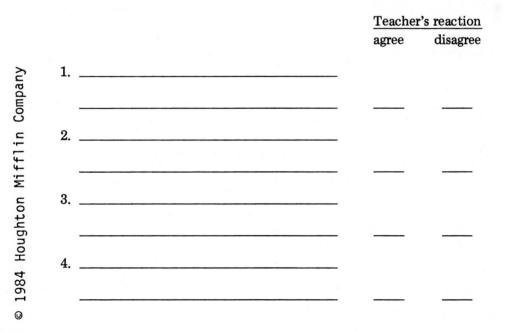

Teacher's reaction
agree   disagree

1. _____

   _____   ____   ____

2. _____

   _____   ____   ____

3. _____

   _____   ____   ____

4. _____

   _____   ____   ____

5. _____

_____   _____   _____

Exercise 2

Do some audience analysis by asking two people to respond to the following questions about two different topics. Try to select people who differ in age by at least ten years, who are not fellow students, and who have different interests.

Topic A: The rapid growth of pay TV and educational TV channels and the decline in audience for network TV (ABC, NBC, and CBS)

	First person	Second person
1. How much do these people think they know about the subject?	_____	_____
2. What are a few things they know about the subject?	_____	_____
	_____	_____
	_____	_____
3. What are a few things they would like to know about the subject?	_____	_____
	_____	_____
	_____	_____

Topic B: The effects of busing on the education of children in previously segregated schools

1. How much do these people think they know about the subject?	_____	_____
	_____	_____

2. What are a few things they
   know about the subject?

   _____   _____

   _____   _____

   _____   _____

3. What are a few things they
   would need to know about the
   subject?

   _____   _____

   _____   _____

   _____   _____

Exercise 3

Select three magazines with which you are familiar, think of an appropriate topic for each, and describe the audience who would read each article.
In your description of the readers, include their probable age range,
educational level, economic status, knowledge of the subject, and values.
Do not go on to the second part of this exercise until you have completed your description of readers for each magazine.

Magazine 1: _____

Your topic: _____

Description of readers: _____

_____

_____

Magazine 2: _____

Your topic: _____

Description of readers: _____

_____

_____

Magazine 3: _____

Your topic: _____

Description of readers: _____

_____

_____

In this part of the exercise go to your college or public library and locate the latest edition of *The Writer's Market* (Cincinnati: Writer's Digest Books), which lists all major American publications that accept manuscripts. The listing for each magazine describes the audience for whom the editors of the magazine intend the articles. Compare the descriptions of the audiences offered there with your descriptions.

Magazine 1: _____

Description of the audience in *Writer's Market*: _____

_____

_____

Differences and similarities between the *Writer's Market* description and

yours: _____

_____

_____

Magazine 2: _____

Description of the audience in *Writer's Market*: _____

_____

_____

Differences and similarities between the *Writer's Market* description and

yours: _____

_____

_____

Magazine 3: _____

Description of the audience in *Writer's Market:* _____

_____

_____

Differences and similarities between the *Writer's Market* description and

yours: _____

_____

_____

Exercise 4

Finding a way to interest some audiences in your writing can be a challenge. For the topics and audiences listed below, can you think of a way to interest these readers? If possible, work with several other writers to find a solution or strategy.

Topic	Audience	Way to interest this audience
1. A family skiing vacation in Aspen, Colorado	a community college sophomore in the midwest majoring in business	_____ _____ _____
	a teacher of freshman composition	_____ _____

	a California high school student who is an avid surfer	_____ _____
2. The influence of TV coverage on presidential elections	a student in your writing course	_____ _____ _____
	a newly arrived immigrant to the United States	_____
	a professor of communications	_____ _____
3. A comparison of the two best rock groups now performing	your composition teacher	_____ _____
	readers of *Time*	_____ _____
	adult readers of your local newspaper	_____ _____ _____

Exercise 5

Listed below are five topics. Describe an appropriate audience for each. After listing audiences for these topics, write five topics of your own choosing and describe appropriate audiences for those topics.

Topic   Appropriate audience

1. The rising crime rate in small towns   _____

                                                      _____

                                                          _____

2. Advantages of large shopping malls   _____

                                                          _____

                                                          _____

3. Reasons for the popularity of
"M.A.S.H."   _____

                                                          _____

                                                          _____

4. Vacation traveling by plane vs. by car   _____

                                                          _____

                                                          _____

5. Current unemployment rates   _____

                                                          _____

                                                          _____

6. _____   _____

                                                          _____

7. _____   _____

                                                          _____

                                                          _____

8. _____   _____

_____

_____

9. _____   _____

_____

_____

10. _____   _____

_____

_____

Exercise 6

For many areas of interest, there are several competing magazines. For example, *Time, Newsweek,* and *U.S. News & World Report* are all weekly news magazines. Competing magazines focus on coin collecting, home decorating, video games, fashion, and hundreds of other specialized areas. Select a field or area of interest and find two or three competing magazines devoted to it. Analyze the audience for each of the competing magazines. Are they the same or are they different? What clues did you find that indicate differences?

Field of interest: _____

Magazines selected for analysis: _____

_____

Similarities and differences in the audience for each magazine: _____

_____

_____

_____

Purpose

Exercise 1

Although you would usually do some planning in order to generate information about several aspects of a subject, sometimes you can look at the subject and see at once several hypotheses you might write about. Try doing so for the subjects listed below.

Subject	Hypotheses
Frozen TV dinners	_____
	_____
	_____
Federal aid to college students	_____
	_____
	_____
Zoos	_____
	_____
	_____
Problems of Vietnam veterans	_____
	_____
	_____
Jogging	_____
	_____
	_____

Exercise 2

Think about any writing that you've done in the last few years, including letters to friends and family, papers for high school and college, business reports or memos, applications, or letters of request or inquiry. List the purpose of five of these pieces of writing.

	Type of writing	Purpose
1.	_____	_____
2.	_____	_____
3.	_____	_____
4.	_____	_____
5.	_____	_____

Exercise 3

As we all know, the same subject can be written about in different ways, depending on the writer's purpose. To gain some practice in viewing a subject with different purposes in mind, read the following excerpt from *Time* and then answer the questions at the end of the article. If possible, work with several other writers and discuss some possible answers to each question.

When schoolchildren at Southern California's Antelope Valley High play hooky, they often are in hot water by bedtime. Every afternoon at 5:15 the school's computer begins phoning 30-second reports to the parents of youngsters who have skipped class that day. After a year of operation, the machine has helped bring down the truancy rate by 64%.

Principal Dale Johnson adapted the computerized tattletale from a similar device used by Sears, Roebuck to call customers. Some 50 school districts across the country have expressed interest in the gadget; the New York City and Chicago school systems recently purchased at least eight machines each. The $8,600 Telsols quickly earn their keep in schools that receive state funds on the basis of pupil attendance. Says Chicago Truant Officer Walter Bryant: "If we raise a district's attendance by nine students a day, we can pay for the machine in less than a year." Bryant believes that the computer can only supplement, not replace, regular truant officers. Officials still must track down children who outsmart the machines by giving out phony home phone numbers or answering the phone themselves. (*Time*, March 7, 1983)

1. If you were a principal of a school in another state and your purpose was to ask the district school board for money to buy one of the machines described in this article, what would your thesis be?

   _____

   _____

   _____

2. If you were a parent protesting the installation of one of these systems because it seemed so impersonal and ineffective, what would your thesis be?

   _____

   _____

   _____

3. If you were a local store owner advocating the purchase of this system because you wanted to reduce shoplifting in your store by truants, what would your thesis be?

   _____

   _____

   _____

Exercise 4

Assume that you are a teacher in an inner city high school in a big city. You are disturbed by the vandalism to your school building and have been asked to address the school board on the causes of vandalism. How would you achieve your purpose? Take some planning notes as you think about your purpose. Compose several hypotheses that you might be able to support, then choose the one that seems best to reflect your purpose. Then draft a short paragraph that you would send to the school board. If possible, form a small group with several other writers and have the group suggest revisions that would make the draft more effective.

Notes: _____

_____

_____

_____

_____

_____

_____

Hypotheses: _____

_____

_____

Chosen hypothesis: _____

Draft: _____

_____

_____

_____

_____

_____

_____

_____

_____

Evaluation Report

1. What is the purpose of the paragraph? _____

   _____

   _____

2. What aspects of the paragraph help to achieve this purpose? _____

   _____

   _____

   _____

3. How can the writer achieve this purpose more effectively? _____

   _____

   _____

   _____

   _____

   Revise the paragraph: _____

   _____

   _____

   _____

   _____

   _____

   _____

   _____

2
Planning

THINKING-IN-WRITING VERSUS THINKING-AND-THEN-WRITING

If you use writing to help you think through your ideas as you plan, you are "thinking-in-writing." If you plan everything mentally and then use writing mainly to record your thoughts, you are "thinking-and-then-writing." These are two very different ways to use writing and to plan a writing task. To see the difference, try the two exercises included here to determine how effective each approach is for you as a writer.

Thinking-and-Then-Writing

Assume that your Uncle Arnie has invited you to spend your two-week winter break at his ranch in Texas. Although you like Uncle Arnie, you stayed at the ranch several times in the past and didn't find it too exciting. You know that Uncle Arnie would like to see you. On the other hand, you have tentative plans with several friends to go skiing in Colorado if you can find a ride.

Decide whether you will accept Uncle Arnie's invitation and write a short response to him. Plan the whole response mentally. When you have a clear idea of what you are going to say, write your response.

First Draft:

_____

_____

_____

_____

_____

_____

_____

_____

Thinking-in-Writing

Assume that your old friend Cindy has written to you to ask a favor.
Istvan, a Hungarian student she met last year when she was traveling in
Europe, is coming to the United States to enroll in the graduate school
of another university in your state. He will be arriving three weeks before
he is expected to be there and would like a place to stay and a chance to
learn a bit about American life and culture. As his English is not yet
fluent, he would also like someone to practice with. Those three weeks
happen to be a particularly busy period for you and you don't have any
suggestions for people with whom he can stay. But Cindy is a good friend,
and she rarely asks people to go out of their way unless there is a good
reason. She did mention that Istvan has had to surmount many obstacles
to come to the U.S. but has succeeded because of his determination to
get here.

Decide whether or not you will agree to invite Istvan and help him
learn more about America. Use writing to help you plan by taking notes
as you think-in-writing, by writing sentences, or perhaps by writing a
rough draft that helps you decide what you are going to say.

Thinking-in-writing notes or draft:

_____

_____

_____

_____

_____

_____

_____

_____

Evaluating "Thinking-and-Then-Writing" Versus "Thinking-in-Writing"

1. Which planning strategy allowed you to complete the task more quickly? Why?

    _____

    _____

2. Which planning strategy helped you to write a better finished response? Why?

    _____

    _____

3. What major differences did you find in the two planning strategies?

    _____

    _____

4. Which strategy seems more helpful for you? Why?

    _____

    _____

Compare your responses to the above questions with another writer's. What are the differences and similarities between your answers and the other writer's?

Differences: _____

_____

_____

Similarities: _____

_____

_____

USING MEMORY IN WRITING

Code Words

This exercise focuses on finding code words, words that identify broad areas or topics one can search through looking for information to shape into a subject.

Listed below are twelve possibilities that may be code words for you. In the space after each code word, try to write several phrases to see if the word unlocks memories you can explore. If the possibilities seem rich, put a plus in the evaluation column at the right. If the word doesn't jog your memory with possibilities, put a minus in the evaluation column.

Topic	Evaluation (+ or −)
1. Sunday mornings _____	
_____	_____
2. Death of a close relative _____	
_____	_____
3. Dawn _____	
_____	_____
4. My favorite childhood book _____	
_____	_____
5. Fishing _____	
_____	_____
6. Money _____	
_____	_____
7. Illness _____	
_____	_____

8. Car accident _____

_____　　_____

9. Flowers _____

_____　　_____

10. School rules _____

_____　　_____

11. Planes _____

_____　　_____

12. Music _____

_____　　_____

It is also important to find your own code words. Listed below are suggestions for areas to explore. Your answers may be personal code words. Follow the same procedure you used in the first half of this exercise and jot down a few phrases after each word. If those possibilities seem rich with potential, put a plus in the evaluation column; if the possibilities seem limited or restricted, put a minus in the evaluation column.

Area or topic	Evaluation (+ or −)

1. A place where you have gone on vacation:

_____　　_____

2. A relative you particularly like or dislike:

_____　　_____

3. A national event that affected you in some

way: _____

_____　　_____

4. A sport that you've played: _____

_____　　_____

5. A place that you enjoy: _____

   _____   _____

6. A topic you often discuss or feel strongly

   about: _____

   _____   _____

7. A holiday you particularly enjoy or dislike:

   _____   _____

8. A problem that is or should be a major concern

   in our society: _____

   _____   _____

Brainstorming

Exercise 1

The selections below are the results of ten to fifteen minutes of brain-storming by two students on some of the suggestions for code words listed in the exercises above. Form a small group with several other writers and read the records of these students' brainstorming. Then answer the questions following each piece of writing.

COLLEGE

Registration day—lines and more lines
forms to fill out
language confusing
too many numbers to remember
course schedule
adviser seemed too rushed to really help. Besides, how does she know
   what I really want to study?
Why didn't I have a choice of teachers?
finding classrooms the first day was the major problem, trying to look
   like I knew where I was going
people are really friendlier than I thought they would be
teachers seem helpful
physics prof expects us to spend all our free time doing problems

How do I get to meet the people sitting around me?
different notebooks for different courses, good idea
need a system to organize myself
homework so far isn't overwhelming, but I can see that college is going
    to require a lot more study time
people here seem really serious about learning
someday we're all going to be professionals out there and need to know
    our job
fortunately, I'm not going to be a brain surgeon, but engineers have big
    responsibilities too, so I'll need to know my stuff too
co-oping is going to be helpful
at college, you need to study, but you also need to try out your field, to
    experience it
a friend in education says she won't try being in front of a class for several
    years, so co-oping is really a unique opportunity to see if it's what I
    want to do
co-oping in college is also to gain experience, to understand why I'll be
    learning what is in the books and the lab manuals
still not sure about that physics course, will I really need to know all that?

1. List some images and ideas that seem to cluster together. _____

_____

_____

_____

2. List two possible subjects in this cluster. _____

_____

_____

3. Select one of these subjects and answer the following questions.

   a. Subject: _____

   b. How significant is this subject? _____

_____

   c. How interesting is this subject? _____

_____

d. How manageable is this subject? _____

_____   _____

e. Who is the audience for this subject? _____

_____

f. What might the writer's purpose be in writing about this subject?

_____   _____

_____   _____

PLANES

powerful, expensive, efficient

great birds in the sky, shiny metal, gleaming

winging off to vacation places in the sun

wear a coat, board a plane, and in an hour or two, you get off in the sunshine and the warmth

can our bodies adapt so easily?

jet lag is a major problem. How do I tell my body that it's dinnertime
when I just had breakfast?

fly across the ocean, switching big chunks of time

"jet setters"—funny term. why run around the world? showing off their
money?

what did people do before fast travel?

slow, quiet life

stay in your own area, grow up there, maybe die there

now, we don't have roots

families break up, shift away from each other, travel has its disadvantages

people are becoming more and more alike everywhere you go

air fares, too high

why do planes cost so much? fuel costs? but big jumbo jets hold so many
people, small crew, but need lots of training, high pay for pilots

should be lots of competition between companies though

there are so many airlines, how do you pick?

they are all alike, how do you choose between McDonald's and Wendy's,
Eastern and United?

some small differences, sure, but maybe there are too many companies
flying half-full planes

but they fly to different places (do they?)
watching planes as a kid was fun
seemed so important as they taxied around a runway
people getting on and off were so casual, they just came down from the
sky
the smell of fuel, diesel, engine roar, incredible power and sound as they
revved up for take off, whine, metal shine

1. List some images and ideas that seem to cluster together. _____

    _____

    ___ _____

    _____

2. List two possible subjects in this cluster. _____

    _____

    _____

3. Select one of these subjects and answer the following questions.

    a. Subject: _____

    b. How significant is this subject? _____

    _____

    c. How interesting is this subject? _____

    _____

    d. How manageable is this subject? _____

    _____

    e. Who is the audience for this subject? _____

    _____

    f. What might the writer's purpose be in writing about this subject?

    _____

_____

_____

Exercise 2

Form a small group with several other writers and select one of the code
words from Exercise 1 or start with a different code word selected by
the group. Brainstorm the code word for about ten minutes. Write down
everything that is said by the group. Then look through the list for images
and ideas that seem to cluster together. Find at least three clusters and
list two possible subjects suggested by those clusters.

1. Record of brainstorming session:

_____

_____

_____

_____

_____

_____

_____

_____

_____

_____

2. Clusters and possible subjects:

    a. Cluster 1: _____

_____

Subject 1: _____

_____

Subject 2: _____

_____

b. Cluster 2: _____

_____

Subject 1: _____

_____

Subject 2: _____

_____

c. Cluster 3: _____

_____

Subject 1: _____

_____

Subject 2: _____

_____

Exercise 3

From the list in Exercise 1, select a code word that is particularly sugges-
tive for you. Brainstorm that code word for fifteen minutes by writing
down everything that comes to mind. Then explore the results for possible
subjects.

Code word: _____

Brainstorming: _____

_____

_____

_____

_____

_____

_____

_____

_____

_____

Possible clusters: _____

_____

_____

_____

   Select one of the clusters you've just written down and think of a possible subject. Write a sentence expressing the subject and brainstorm again using this new focus. Some of the ideas and images you generate in this brainstorming session will repeat what you came up with in your first session.

Cluster: _____

Subject: _____

_____

Brainstorming: _____

_____

_____

_____

_____

_____

_____

_____

_____

_____

_____

_____

Freewriting

Exercise 1

In the two examples included here, the student writers were freewriting for about fifteen minutes. Act as an editor or coach and suggest a possible subject evident in each of these freewritings. Has the writer found enough material for a short essay, or should the writer try a more focused brainstorming session or more freewriting?

GRANDMA

Death, grandma, innocence, religion, habits, holy water at windows during a thunderstorm, cautious worrier, loving, distant, regret, wish I'd seen her more, I've lost the chance, she taught, I could have learned, e.g., crotcheting, knitting, serving, being close, sick, illness, cancer, prognosis, operation and she'll be fine, chemotherapy, hospital, home, hospital, home, "You're healthy," he said, out of it, collapsed, in the hospital again, she's sick, why didn't I see her when I was there/home, I regret, can't forget, "How is she, Mom?" the same, the same, she hasn't changed, she's losing her hair, Sandra couldn't find her wig, "Is grandpa okay?" As can be expected, he worried, she said, "Harry, I'm glad I married you," "Well, it took you long enough to figure that out—42 years," he was glad to hear it though I bet, his dry humor, I love them both. "How is she, Mom?" the same, the same. Baby born, she's Lindsay, God, please don't take her, not an exchange. "How is she, Mom?" the same, the same, go home Kelly if you can, try getting rides, "Really, Mom? You got the plane tickets? Great!" see you there, Sunday home, Monday night "When can I see Grandma?" Bye, Colleen. Bye Steven. Mom why were you two laughing. "I have something to tell you," she said. "I know and you weren't laughing. You two were choking back tears. It's ironic how those two things sound so much alike." My tears, remembering, regretting. A graveside visit. "Why can't she have a stone?" "They don't let you put the big ones up anymore" "It's not fair. She deserved at least that. She probably would have thought it a waste of money though. "Wanna see Grandpa?" Yes. Life goes on, but not always happily. (Kelly Devlin—student writer)

What is a possible subject you'd suggest for this writer? _____

_____

What might the writer make use of from the freewriting for this subject?

_____

_____

Does the writer need more material? _____

Any suggestions for more material? _____

_____

SUNDAY MORNINGS

Sunday mornings, Ah! Peaceful, restful mornings shared with my room-mate, coffee and doughnuts, and the Sunday paper. (of course). Easy quiet times where you can sleep as late as you want and wake up to the smell of coffee perking. Sunday comics read in your bathrobe until noon. Ah!

But, open the curtains of the sliding glass door and the world comes alive. Across the street, the infamous church looms with its steeple pointing uprighteously high in the sky. Cars fill the parking lot, filling up the guilt in your mind. I should go to church. You would feel so much better afterward. You went all the time when you were little. But things were different then. Weekends lasted forever. You were up at the crack of dawn and there wasn't anything on T.V. anyway.

Now things are so busy. Never enough time in the day for things you need to do. Rush, Rush, Rush. Sunday is the only day to sleep-in and relax. After all, isn't Sunday the day of rest? Oh well, I'll sleep-in this Sunday and go to church next weekend. (Carol Phillabaum—student writer)

What is a possible subject you'd suggest for this writer? _____

_____

What might the writer make use of from the freewriting for this subject?

_____

_____

Does the writer need more material? _____

Any suggestions for more material? _____

_____

_____   _____

Exercise 2

Practice freewriting without a code word or focus in mind by writing for ten minutes. Once you start, don't let your pen or pencil stop until the time is up. If nothing specific comes to mind, keep writing the same word or phrase over and over until something else occurs to you. Don't edit what you write or attempt to correct it in any way. Just keep writing. When you are finished, answer the questions listed below. They should help you evaluate the effectiveness of freewriting as a strategy for you.

_____

_____   _____

_____

_____   _____

_____

_____

_____

_____

_____

_____

_____

_____

_____

_____

Do you enjoy or dislike freewriting? Why? _____

_____

Did the freewriting you just completed turn up some useful material?

_____

How effective is freewriting as a technique for you? _____

_____

Do you intend to use freewriting as a planning strategy in future writing?

_____ Why? _____

_____

_____

Exercise 3

Practice freewriting with a focus by choosing a code word of your own or selecting one from the exercise 1 above. Write for ten minutes with that code word as your focus. After you finish freewriting, form a small group, if possible, with several other writers and answer the questions below. These questions are designed to help you find a subject, audience, and purpose for a future writing based on your freewriting.

Freewriting

_____

_____

_____

_____

_____

_____

_____

_____

_____

_____

_____

_____

_____

Subject

1. What is a possible subject in this writing? _____

_____

_____

2. Is the subject sufficiently focused yet? _____ If not, can you

suggest a focus? _____

_____

3. What is the most interesting and/or significant aspect of this subject?

_____

_____

4. What aspect of this subject needs more development? _____

_____

_____

Audience

1. Who is the primary audience for this subject? _____

_____

2. What general attitudes and information does this audience have?

_____

_____

3. Is there any other audience for this subject? _____

_____

_____

4. How might the writing be adapted to this audience? _____

_____

_____

Purpose

1. What hypothesis does the writer want to prove? _____

_____

_____

2. What is the writer's thesis? _____

_____

_____

Keeping a Journal

Practice keeping a journal by making three daily entries here. If you have no special ideas, thoughts, or events to record for the day, try responding to one or more of the following suggestions:

1. Write about something you have just learned in one of your classes.
2. Speculate on where you might be and what you might be doing ten years from now.
3. What would it be like if everyone in the world were shorter (or taller) than you?
4. Of all the ongoing problems of environmental pollution, nuclear freezes, strife in the Middle East, current elections, inflation, unemployment, the rights of minorities and women, violence and crime, and so on, which is getting more attention than it really deserves? Why?
5. What is your favorite food? When and where do you like to consume it?
6. If you could make one rule that would be strictly enforced in the community around you, what would it be? Why would you want that rule?
7. Jobs or professions can be categorized in several ways—as dangerous or safe, as high paying or low paying, as rewarding and interesting or dull, as respected or not. Discuss the kinds of job classifications that you think are important and include some examples.

8. Some people say that our names are very important because they influence other people's thoughts about us. What is your opinion about
this?
9. What is your favorite kind of vacation? Why?
10. Describe a recent movie, TV program, or concert that you've seen.
How good was it? Why?

_____

USING OBSERVATION IN WRITING

Lookout Spots

To find a lookout spot, you can begin by locating an area and then by
finding a particular spot in that area from which to observe. Listed below

are ten locations or possible places to try. Select one of these as well as a location of your choice. Walk around both of these locations for awhile and note some likely lookout spots in each.

1. Suggestions for locations
   a. A place to observe a means of transportation (for example, buses, trains, subways, cars, bikes, boats, or planes)
   b. A nearby building of historical interest
   c. A local business where something is produced (for example, a newspaper plant, a restaurant kitchen, a factory)
   d. A place where a service is offered (for example, a doctor's office, a library, a student counseling office, a copy shop, a welfare agency, a hospital, a college registrar's office, or a police station)
   e. A local landmark (for example, a new office building, a bridge, a lake, a monument, or a park)
   f. An amusement place (for example, a theater, a video arcade, or a pizza parlor)
   g. A sports facility (for example, a skating rink, a basketball court, a football field, or a tennis court)
   h. A quiet natural setting removed from urban noise
   i. A place you pass every day (for example, the street in front of your residence, a store, a college classroom building, or a place of work)
   j. A shopping mall or street with stores

2. Your selection _____
   Explore this location and note some likely lookout spots:

   a. _____

   b. _____

   c. _____

   d. _____

   e. _____

3. Go out for a walk and wander around until you find a possible location with some lookout spots.

   The location you selected: _____
   Some likely lookout spots:

   a. _____

b. _____

c. _____

d. _____

e. _____

Scouting

Working with another writer, visit one of the lookout spots listed above. Spend at least twenty minutes writing down everything you see, hear, taste, touch, and smell. Begin on your own and don't compare notes with the other writer until you have both finished. Use words that specifically describe your sensory impressions of size, color, sound, shape, texture, feel, and so on. Begin with a phrase or two that gives the dominant impression of the lookout spot.

Lookout spot: _____

Dominant impression: _____

_____

Sensory impressions: _____

_____

_____

_____

When you have spent about twenty minutes doing this by yourself, compare your lists with those of the other writer.

Are your dominant impressions the same? _____
If not, do they lead both of you to observe different things in the same

scene? _____

How do your lists differ? _____

_____

What can each of you contribute to the other's list that was overlooked

or not observed by that person? _____

_____

_____

Analyze your lookout spot by answering the following questions:

1. Is this lookout spot a promising place for more observation? Why?

    _____

    _____

2. What possible subjects occur to you after observing this place? _____

    _____

    _____

3. Who might be an appropriate audience? _____

    _____

    _____

4. For what purpose might you write about this subject? _____

    _____

    _____

Mapping

1. Choose a small area of the room you are in to map spatially. Using a
    sheet of blank paper, frame the scene to indicate what is to be in-
    cluded. Then draw the major objects in that spot and label them.
    Finally, catalog the minor details not included on your map. Note
    anything that is not in the drawing that might be useful.
2. Go to an area in your school library where there is generally a lot of
    activity. On a blank sheet of paper with a frame drawn around the area

to be mapped, map the pattern of activity you see. The following questions may help you to observe this activity.

  a. In what directions are people most frequently headed as they enter the area? Where or what are they going to or headed toward?
  b. What objects are moved about? What directions are these objects moved in?
  c. What direction do people go when they are exiting the area?
  d. Where are the areas of least activity?
  e. What kinds of activities are people engaged in in this area? How frequently and in what amounts?

What did you learn from this observation that you weren't aware of earlier?

_____

_____

3. Interview a person who must work with two- or three-dimensional maps (for example, a stage set designer, a newspaper layout person, an engineer or scientist who must draw an object or action, or a sports coach who must use play diagrams. Ask to see a typical map used (or drawn) by that person and note in the space below the kinds of information included in the map and how the map is used.

_____

_____

_____

_____

_____

_____

4. Go back to the lookout spot you scouted in the scouting exercise above and draw a map indicating both the spatial relationships among the objects and, if possible, the kinds and patterns of activity in that spot. Note any unique features also. When you are done, add details and notes that help you record what was not drawn on the map. Look back over your map and evaluate what mapping has added to your previous suggestions for subject, audience, and purpose. Building on what you

have already noted, add to or revise your suggestions for subject, audience, and purpose.

a. Subject: _____

_____

b. Audience: _____

_____

c. Purpose: _____

_____

Speculating

To practice speculating from a different perspective, try the following two exercises.

1. Assume that you are speculating on video-arcade games. The speculations listed below look at video-arcade games as an object, as an action, and as a network. From which perspective is each statement made? Write "object," "action," or "network" in the space provided.

_____ a. The flashing lights, sound, and even synthesized voice commands of some games appeal to several of our senses simultaneously.

_____ b. Video-arcade games are, like television, placing us in front of a screen, and eventually we may have TV sets that we also respond to and interact with.

_____ c. Video-arcade games are highly complex machines run by sophisticated computer programs which, some say, result in very simple-minded games. Others view the games as equally sophisticated.

_____ d. The first arcade games were boxes that players stood in front of, but a few of the newer ones are designed for the player to step inside.

_____ e. Most video-arcade games offer as options buttons to push, wheels to turn, and joysticks to manipulate.

_____ f. Some video-arcade games maintain their popularity for months and continue to bring in money for the designer; other games have a brief spurt of popularity and then are moved out.

      g. Like pinball machines, video-arcade games are popular amusements, and like the older craze for pinball, some people become addicted to them.

      h. The most popular video-arcade games share common characteristics with popular science fiction movies in that they have an identifiable character or imaginative graphics and unusual themes.

2. Using the subject you have been exploring by means of scouting and mapping, develop the same subject further by speculation. Answer the following questions about the subject by letting yourself speculate freely. If you're stuck, use the techniques of brainstorming or freewriting that you tried earlier.

  a. Speculate on your subject as an object by thinking about it as an object or as an unmoving state of things at rest. What is it?

_____

_____

  b. Speculate on your subject as it moves, changes, and progresses.

_____

_____

  c. Speculate on your subject as it fits into a network with other things, connects with them, and is part of a series.

_____

_____

_____

USING RESEARCH IN WRITING

Search Questions

To formulate some search questions, examine the ten topics listed below and ask yourself at least three questions about each topic. To help formulate questions, start with one of the question words: *who, what, where, when, why,* and *how.* Or, create questions that compare or contrast aspects of the topic, analyze its parts, break it down into groups, define a term, describe a process, and so on.

1. Tournament of Roses

   Question 1: _____

   _____

   Question 2: _____

   _____

   Question 3: _____

   _____

2. Braille reading method for the blind

   Question 1: _____

   _____

   Question 2: _____

   _____

   Question 3: _____

   _____

3. The Nobel Prize

   Question 1: _____

   _____

   Question 2: _____

   _____

   Question 3: _____

   _____

4. Weather forecasting

   Question 1: _____

   _____

   Question 2: _____

   _____

   Question 3: _____

   _____

5. A community service in your area (for example, a service for senior citizens, recent immigrants, shut-ins, alcoholics, or single parents)

   Question 1: _____

   _____

   Question 2: _____

   _____

   Question 3: _____

   _____

6. Photography

   Question 1: _____

   _____

   Question 2: _____

   _____

   Question 3: _____

   _____

7. Water or air pollution

   Question 1: _____

_____

Question 2: _____

_____

Question 3: _____

_____

8. The current job market for your present or proposed major field

Question 1: _____

_____

Question 2: _____

_____

Question 3: _____

_____

9. Hand calculators

Question 1: _____

_____

Question 2: _____

_____

Question 3: _____

_____

10. Tennis

Question 1: _____

_____

Question 2: _____

_____

Question 3: _____

_____

Interviewing

Exercise 1

The following questions were asked by the well-known journalist Eric Sevareid as he interviewed some notable people for TV. Study his questions to see not only what he asks, but also how he asks his questions. (All excerpts are from *Conversations with Eric Sevareid.*)

In an interview with Daniel Patrick Moynihan, a former ambassador to the United Nations, Sevareid asked the following:

Sevareid: Mr. Moynihan you went into the UN because you had written and said we must stand up to this assault, we can no longer go on with a dignified, long suffering silence even though there are small countries attacking us. And then, after just a few months, you're out of the job. Why did you leave?

What is effective or ineffective about this question? _____

_____

_____

Another question asked of Mr. Moynihan:

Sevareid: You've been very diplomatically quiet about your leaving the UN. Conventional wisdom in Washington has it that the man who put you there, Mr. Kissinger, is the man who in effect put you out. Is there anything you want to say about this?

What is effective or ineffective about this question? _____

_____

_____

In an interview with Eric Hoffer, a retired longshoreman and author:

Sevareid: How do your friends on the waterfront treat you, knowing that you write books?

Hoffer: Oh, every longshoreman knows that if he tried hard enough he could write like Shakespeare. I have often been told by longshoremen that if they did what I do, which is to bury myself in printed matter when there is no work, they could write, too.

Sevareid: Well, when I was young and worked in gangs and teams and one thing and another, the idea that I was a kind of kid-writer, a newspaperman, a pseudo-intellectual or something, created a certain alienation with the fellows.

What is effective or ineffective about Sevareid's question and response?

_____

_____

_____

Another question asked of Mr. Hoffer:

Sevareid: I wanted to get into the business of intellectuals in this country you've written about so much. I think in one of your books you say that a mass society like ours is not conducive to producing an effective or powerful intellectual group. But in your last book you say the intellectual is really coming into his own in this country. Aren't you contradicting yourself here?

What is effective or ineffective about this question? _____

_____

_____

In an interview with Walter Lippmann, the political analyst:

Sevareid: What have been your own impressions of President Johnson's method of conducting this office [of President]?

Lippmann: My feeling about that is this: When President Kennedy was murdered the situation abroad and at home was in a state of crisis. His own policies were blocked at home and they were frustrated abroad. The country was very deeply and bitterly divided about him. There was sectional feeling. There was class feeling. There was racial feeling. President Johnson is by nature a healing man, a man who heals. That's been his function, his mission, in his first hundred days.

Sevareid: Are you saying, in effect, that while Johnson may not have the fervent phalanx of admirers in the country that Kennedy had he has fewer enemies?

What is effective or ineffective about these questions? _____

_____

_____

Exercise 2

Read the following excerpts from two interviews and evaluate the interviewers' abilities by answering the questions that follow each excerpt.

The questions posed by Eric Sevareid in Exercise 1 were part of a TV series of interviews with noted Americans. The excerpt included here is from another interview in that series, this one with Robert Maynard Hutchins, President of the University of Chicago.

Sevareid: Should someone going into medical school be expected to have a lot more liberal education than is the case now?

Hutchins: Yes. At the University of Chicago, for a while, a student couldn't specialize in any field until he had passed 14 liberal arts examinations. Those who passed carried through their lives at least some faint recollection of things outside the discipline in which they came to specialize.

Sevareid: I think you once said that you weren't particularly concerned about the economic conditions of the country or the material well-being of people. But aren't they pretty fundamental to the kind of education you want us to pursue?

Hutchins: At the bottom of the depression during the 1930's I tried to tell students that there are other things in life besides financial success. Most of them had a big headstart anyway. They didn't have to worry about personal economic problems. What I was concerned about was their moral sense. I didn't see anything come out of the depression, from an educational point of view, that was harmful. Incidentally the University of Chicago was, I think, a much better institution by the end of the depression than at the onset.

Sevareid: You stripped away a lot of things like football and created a national uproar.

Hutchins: Some of the faculty members I brought to the university were young men with a completely fresh outlook. We simply said: "Why don't we see what makes sense and what doesn't." Football didn't, of course, stand very high. The student body immediately improved.

How well prepared was the interviewer? _____

_____

How would you describe the interviewer's attitude—positive? friendly?

apologetic? Which attitudes are helpful or effective? _____

_____

_____

Is the interviewer well organized? Does he proceed in an orderly way?

How can you tell that? _____

_____

_____

Does the conversation develop naturally? _____

_____

_____

What effective techniques does the interviewer use? _____

_____

_____

_____

How useful were the answers? Did they answer the questions being asked?

_____

_____

_____

If you were offering advice to this interviewer on how to improve his

techniques, what would you suggest? _____

_____

_____

_____

In an interview with Calvin Trillin, an author of books, newspaper articles, and columns for *The New Yorker*, his wife, Alice Trillin, asked the following questions:

Alice: Let's begin by talking about how you approach a "U.S. Journal" story for *The New Yorker* once you arrive in the city you are going to write about.

Calvin: First I have to have some idea, even if it's a vague one, of what interests me about the situation before I get there. I'm probably better off if the idea *is* vague because I don't want to have too many pre-conceptions about what the story is: after all, the story I have in mind before I arrive may not actually work out to be a story.

Alice: How often do your ideas for stories change?

Calvin: They change fairly often. Sometimes the entire subject changes, but more often the approach changes. . . .

Alice: What do you do if you get someplace and find out the story isn't there at all?

Calvin: Well, I recently did a story in Utah that was unusual because I changed the subject after I got home. I went out originally to do a story on a kind of maverick, self-taught scientist who was having trouble with a town in Utah where he was conducting experiments that he said would end the energy crisis. . . . As it turned out in this case, the town and the way it allotted and used space were terribly interesting. . . . As a result, I didn't use very much of what I had researched about the scientist, but instead I used a lot about the context. So it ended up to be a story about space in Wendover, Utah.

Alice: That's interesting to me because I think it was your least successful story this year. Is that because you hadn't done the right research?

Calvin: Right. Even though I had gathered a lot of material about the town because it was what interested me most, I really hadn't done it in as systematic a way as I would have if I had actually started out reporting on the town or had changed my mind while I was out there . . . . The more you know about a situation, the more small details and knowledge you have beyond what you seem to need, the better you can write about it. (Alice Trillin, "A Writer's Process: A Conversation with Calvin Trillin," *Journal of Basic Writing*)

How well prepared was the interviewer? _____

_____

How would you describe the interviewer's attitude—positive? friendly?

apologetic? Which attitudes are helpful or effective? _____

_____

_____

Is the interviewer well organized? Does she proceed in an orderly way?

How can you tell that? _____

_____

_____

Does the conversation develop naturally? _____

_____

_____

What effective techniques does the interviewer use? _____

_____

_____

_____

How useful were the answers? Did they answer the questions being asked?

_____

_____

_____

If you were offering advice to this interviewer on how to improve her

techniques, what would you suggest? _____

_____

_____

_____

Exercise 3

Select one of the search questions you formulated earlier. Try to learn
more about it by interviewing and answer the following questions:

1. Search question: _____

_____

2. Who might you interview on the subject?

   a. Expert: _____

   b. Participant: _____

   c. Information broker: _____

3. Select one of these people to interview and formulate some interview
   questions.

_____

_____

_____

_____

_____

4. Summary of your interview:

_____

_____

_____

_____

5. Evaluate your responses:

_____

_____

_____

_____

_____

Reading

Exercise 1

To use reading as a planning strategy, select one of the topics listed below and find five things to read on this topic. As you read each selection, jot down aspects of the subject that might interest you further, serve as a subject to write about, or help you formulate search questions.

To find reading material, you can consult newspaper indexes such as the index to the *New York Times*, magazine indexes such as *The Readers'*

Guide to Periodical Literature, and book indexes such as your library's card catalog or the subject index of the most recent *Books in Print*. Sometimes, you will find that one selection will lead you to others.

Possible topics

Candy or snack food   Frisbee
Insomnia   Vocational rehabilitation
Aerobic exercise or dancing   Greeting cards
U.S. space shuttle program   Three Mile Island
Hitch-hiking   Plastic surgery

The topic you selected: _____
Materials to read on the topic:

a. _____

b. _____

c. _____

d. _____

e. _____

Notes from your reading:

_____

_____

_____

_____

_____

  Use the search question you formulated at the beginning of this section on using research in writing and then developed through interviewing. Develop it further through reading. List some materials to read, take planning notes as you read, and then add to your notes on subject, audience, and purpose for this topic.

Your search question: _____

_____

Materials to read on this topic: _____

_____

_____

_____

_____

Notes on your reading: _____

_____

_____

_____

_____

MIXING SOURCES AND STRATEGIES

1. In this chapter you have been practicing planning strategies using code
    words, lookout spots, and search questions. Write an essay based on the
    planning notes that you've developed from one of these topics.
2. Using a combination of planning strategies, plan a paper on one of the
    following topics:
    a. Computerized dating services
    b. Japanese technology
    c. A service organization on campus or in your area
    d. OPEC
    e. CB radios
    f. Halloween
    g. Parades
    h. Recycling efforts
    i. State lotteries

    j. (Your choice): _____

COMPARING AND EVALUATING PLANNING STRATEGIES

Some planning strategies that work well for you may be less effective for other writers. To see how varied different writers' responses are, form a small group with several other writers and answer this survey by indicating how many members of your group find the strategy very useful, how many find it somewhat useful, and how many find it not useful at all. As your group discusses its answers, note some reasons for each writer's evaluation.

Strategy	Not useful at all	Somewhat useful	Very useful
1. Brainstorming			

Why? _____

_____

2. Freewriting _____

Why? _____

_____

3. Journal writing _____

Why? _____

_____

4. Scouting _____

Why? _____

_____

5. Mapping _____

Why? _____

_____

6. Speculating _____

Why? _____

_____

7. Interviewing _____

Why? _____ _____

_____

8. Reading _____

Why? _____

_____

3
Drafting

WRITING THE FIRST DRAFT

One way to impose order on a collection of material is to make a scratch outline that sorts the information into possible clusters. Then find connections among the groups.

Making a Scratch Outline

Exercise 1

In order to sort information, you need to find sorting techniques that work well. Some people skim through a list, assigning the same number or letter to similar items; others use a blank sheet of paper to cluster similar items in different locations on the sheet; and other people have still different techniques. Find a technique that works for you and sort the following information from the Bureau of Labor Statistics, U.S. Department of Labor (as reported in *The World Almanac and Book of Facts, 1983*).

First, sort the items into six major types of occupations. Then sort the list into four levels of income. Can you think of a third way to sort the list? Form a small group with several other writers to discuss possible ways to sort the information for the third grouping. As your group is sorting, share the techniques you used when sorting the list individually.

Although you may want to use scratch paper when first forming your clusters, use the space provided here to record your answers.

JOB INFORMATION

Types of jobs	Median earnings per week
Bank tellers	$ 189
Veterinarians	656
Lawyers	546
Roofers	267
Chemical engineers	575
Airplane pilots	530
Cashiers	168
Dentists	1,057
Bookkeepers	227
Librarians	320
Plumbers	404
Postal clerks	400
Barbers	327
Mechanical engineers	540
Cooks and chefs	171
Firefighters	362
Police officers	363
Carpenters	325
Bus drivers	298
Civil engineers	505
Electricians	419
Nurses	332
Truck drivers	517
Pharmacists	463
Electrical engineers	549
Physicians	501

Types of occupations:

a. _____   b. _____

_____   _____

_____   _____

_____   _____

_____   _____

_____   _____

c. _____

d. _____

_____

_____

_____

_____

_____

_____

_____

_____

_____

_____

e. _____

f. _____

_____

_____

_____

_____

_____

_____

_____

_____

Levels of income:

a. _____

b. _____

_____

_____

_____

_____

_____

_____

_____

_____

c. _____

d. _____

_____

_____

_____

_____

_____   _____

_____   _____

_____   _____

Your groupings: _____

a. _____   b. _____

_____   _____

_____   _____

_____   _____

_____   _____

_____   _____

c. _____   d. _____

_____   _____

_____   _____

_____   _____

_____   _____

e. _____   f. _____

_____   _____

_____   _____

_____   _____

_____   _____

Describe three different sorting techniques that you or members of
your group used in the exercises above.

1. _____

_____

2. _____

_____

3. _____

_____

Exercise 2

The following exercise offers more practice in sorting. Included here is
information on the leading U.S. advertisers in 1980 (as reported in *The
World Almanac and Book of Facts, 1983*). First, sort the information so
that you can see how much advertising is done by these companies in
newspapers and on network TV. Break the totals into four groups. For
example, one group might be a list of all the companies which place over
75 percent of their ads in newspapers and on network TV. Then sort the
list, in four groups, to show a relationship between the expenditures for
advertising and the amount of sales. Can you think of a third way to sort
this information? Form a small group with several other writers to discuss
possible ways to sort the information for the third grouping and share
your sorting techniques.

Company	Ad costs (000)	In news-papers (%)	On net-work TV (%)	Sales (000)
Proctor & Gamble	$649,624	1.4	66.1	$11,416,000
Colgate-Palmolive	225,000	2.6	50.5	5,130,464
Heublein	170,000	6.1	36.5	1,921,879
General Foods	410,000	2.9	59.5	6,601,300
Pillsbury	124,026	3.2	55.0	3,301,700
Philip Morris	364,595	24.2	30.5	9,822,300
Ralston, Purina	206,795	1.9	63.8	4,885,000

General Motors	316,000	17.6	41.7	57,728,508
Seagram	152,000	15.4	9.6	2,534,952
R. J. Reynolds	298,524	38.5	3.7	10,354,100
Anheuser-Busch	181,279	1.3	51.2	3,822,400
Ford Motors	280,000	9.9	50.8	37,085,500
Coca-Cola	184,185	4.2	44.7	5,912,600
Chrysler	150,000	12.8	39.5	9,225,300
McDonald's	206,962	-------	41.0	6,226,000
General Mills	171,115	2.1	47.0	4,852,400
PepsiCo	233,400	1.1	55.2	5,975,220

Total percentages of advertising in newspapers and network TV:

a. _____   b. _____

_____   _____

_____   _____

_____   _____

_____   _____

c. _____   d. _____

_____   _____

_____   _____

_____   _____

_____   _____

Relationship between the expenditures for advertising and amount of sales:

a. _____   b. _____

_____   _____

_____   _____

_____   _____

_____   _____

c. _____   d. _____

_____   _____

_____   _____

_____   _____

_____   _____

Your sorting: _____

a. _____   b. _____

_____   _____

_____   _____

_____   _____

_____   _____

c. _____   d. _____

_____   _____

_____   _____

_____   _____

_____   _____

Exercise 3

For practice in sorting and finding connections between groups, use
the collection of facts, figures, and statements on Hong Kong included
here. In this chaotic list, you'll find a number of possibilities for clusters,
and some information will overlap into more than one cluster. When
you've formed clusters, list some possible connections between the
groups.

HONG KONG

Land area: 1,100 sq. kilometers

Hong Kong is a major jewelry center of the world and is said to be the
third biggest retailer of diamonds after the U.S. and Japan. Jade and
pearls are sold abundantly.

Population: 5.1 million, 98.5% are Chinese (mainly immigrants or de-
scendants of immigrants from China)

Hong Kong contains sights from Old China, rickshaws, rice paddies, sam-
pans in the harbor, abacus dealers, and street barbers.

Average per capita income—equivalent of about U.S. $4,600

Number of tourists annually: 2.3 million

There are cricket matches and sailing regattas in Hong Kong.

Some old people still follow the ways and dress of China, but the young
are likely to be dressed in the latest fashions from Paris or Los Angeles

Housing costs range widely, from over Hong Kong $20/sq. ft. when renting
better-class apartments to less than Hong Kong $.50 sq. ft. for poor
workers. A businessman may pay Hong Kong $15,000 to Hong Kong
$25,000/month for an apartment, most of which is reimbursed by his
company. This is about ten times what the average Chinese worker
takes home in wages each month.

In the Westernized shops of Central District, one can find the latest merchandise from Paris, Rome, London, New York, and Tokyo.

In some districts of Hong Kong there are up to 160,000 people per sq. km.
living in cramped, high-rise housing (more than ten times the population density of Tokyo). Almost half the people live in government or
government-aided housing at low rents. The government has housing
projects underway, but this is Hong Kong's greatest social problem.

Tourists shopping in Hong Kong tend to buy jewelry, watches, perfumes,
cameras, optical goods, rosewood furniture, and Asian curios.

Most of Hong Kong's population growth has occurred since the end of the
Second World War. The population went from 600,000 in 1945 to four
million in 1971.

People from Shanghai, most of whom came after 1949, are among Hong
Kong's most prominent manufacturers, businessmen, and financiers.

Most of the early immigrants came illegally, when official attitudes were
tolerant. Now, the government attitude is very strict. Illegal immigrants
are held in transit camps until they can be sent to other countries for
resettlement.

Public housing, education, and social services cannot accommodate heavy
immigration. Slums and shanty towns spring up and are often washed
away during typhoons and spring rains.

250,000 people live in squatter shacks, wood and tin huts dug into hillsides, vacant lots, and roof tops.

Much of Hong Kong's land for agriculture is being taken over by industry.
The manufacturers of textiles and clothing are still Hong Kong's dominant
money earners.

People in Hong Kong seem to be more money-minded than in other places
in the world. The impulse to make money seems to dominate everything. (Gathered from Fodor's *Southeast Asia 1983*)

Clustering information into groups:

Cluster 1 _____

_____

_____

_____

_____

_____

Cluster 2 _____

_____

_____

_____

_____

_____

Cluster 3 _____

_____

_____

_____

_____

_____

_____

Cluster 4 _____

_____

_____

_____

_____

_____

Finding connections between groups:

Possible connections between the groups listed above:

_____

_____

_____

_____

_____

Exercise 4

Use some of the material generated in Chapter 2, when you were practicing planning strategies, to practice clustering. Select one set of materials generated through brainstorming, freewriting, or journal writing and
cluster that material into groups in the space provided below. If you do
not have an available list to work from, you can begin by finding material

on one of the following topics:

alcohol abuse
camping or backpacking
your least favorite chore or responsibility
cartoon characters that you like
a teacher whom you admire
winter
dieting
a recent election
hard rock
jogging or other exercise

Material to be sorted:

_____

_____

_____

_____

_____

_____

_____

_____

_____

_____

_____

Cluster 1: _____

_____

_____

_____

Cluster 2: _____

_____

_____

_____

Cluster 3: _____

_____

_____

_____

Cluster 4: _____

_____

_____

_____

Cluster 5: _____

_____

_____

_____

Defining a Preliminary Hypothesis

Exercise 1

The excerpts included here are essay introductions that tell the reader
what the writer is writing about and why. Read each excerpt and then

answer the questions that follow it.

> During the last decade, as juvenile crime rates have soared, several well-publicized studies have proclaimed that nothing works in rehabilitating young criminals. Indeed, some researchers have argued that early intervention in the lives of delinquents actually harms them.
>
> We disagree. Research that we completed in 1981 shows that at least one approach—a form of rehabilitation therapy—may offer hope for altering delinquent behavior and attitudes. (William McCord and Jose Sanchez, "Curing Criminal Negligence," *Psychology Today*)

1. What is the authors' attitude toward their material? _____

   _____

   _____

2. Express the authors' hypothesis in a statement of purpose. _____

   _____

   _____

3. To what extent is the author's statement restricted, unified, and

   precise? _____

   _____

   _____

4. Speculate on what the rest of the essay will be about. _____

   _____

   _____

   _____

> As medicine prolongs life, unions shorten the work day, governments lower the pension age, and machines take over labor, this world is headed for more and more leisure, and, in my opinion, it had better prepare for it carefully. Maybe today's kids can handle a world without work. My

generation thought of it, but we weren't qualified to handle it even if we'd got it. We found ourselves at a loss when we were faced with a few weeks holidays, although most of us didn't admit it. (Robert Thomas Allen, "A World Without Work," *We Gave You the Electric Toothbrush!*)

1. What is the author's attitude toward his material? _____

   _____

   _____

2. Express the author's hypothesis in a statement of purpose. _____

   _____

   _____

   _____

3. To what extent is the author's statement restricted, unified, and

   precise? _____

   _____

   _____

4. Speculate on what the rest of the essay will be about. _____

   _____

   _____

   _____

Ever since the history-dimmed day when Christopher Columbus, a Genoese male, turned his three ships (*Nina, Pinta,* and *Santa Maria*) toward the United States, men have also played a significant part in the development of our nation. Lord Baltimore, who founded the colony of Maryland for Roman Catholics driven by political persecution from Europe's centuries-old shores, was a man. So was Wyatt Earp, who brought Anglo-Saxon common law into a vast area then in the grip of a *potpourri* of retributive justice, "vigilantism," and the ancient Code Napoleon. Calvin Coolidge, the thirtieth Chief Executive, was male. The list could be extended indefinitely. (John Updike, "The American Man: What of Him?" *Assorted Prose*)

1. What is the author's attitude toward his material? _____

_____

_____

2. Express the author's hypothesis in a statement of purpose. _____

_____

_____

3. To what extent is the author's statement restricted, unified, and

   precise? _____

   _____

   _____

4. Speculate on what the rest of the essay will be about. _____

   _____

   _____

   _____

© 1984 Houghton Mifflin Company

    Of the 100,000 or so chemicals now in use by American industry,
575 are deemed dangerous in large doses by the federal government, and
many of these are known to be associated with catastrophic illness, from
cancer to respiratory and lung disease. Perhaps no class of chemicals is
more subtle and treacherous in its effects, however, than the neurotoxins,
which can damage the human nervous system even in modest doses and
cause a variety of behavioral and emotional symptoms—among them,
hallucinations, loss of memory, confusion, depression, and psychosis.
(Alan Anderson, "Neurotoxic Follies," *Psychology Today*)

1. What is the author's attitude toward his material? _____

_____

_____

2. Express the author's hypothesis in a statement of purpose. _____

_____

_____

_____

3. To what extent is the author's statement restricted, unified, and

precise? _____

_____

_____

_____

4. Speculate on what the rest of the essay will be about. _____

_____

_____

_____

Exercise 2

Included here are the introductions to five student essays. Read the introductions and briefly summarize what the writers are writing about and why they are writing about those subjects.

The Bermuda Triangle is an unsolved mystery that has taken the lives of a lot of men, women, and children, and many planes and ships. Although researchers have worked for years, no definite answer has yet been found to explain the Bermuda Triangle mystery which began in the early Twentieth Century. The theories that scientists have found range from the geological structure of the Bermuda Islands to the effects of the weather, and others have speculated on the possibility of sea serpents and unidentified flying objects. However, both the scientific theories and the strange beliefs about supernatural causes are unsatisfactory solutions because they all fail to solve the disappearances without loose ends or extra details being left over. (Student writer)

1. What is this writer writing about? _____

   _____ _____ _____

   _____ _____

2. Why is this writer writing about this? _____

   _____

   _____ _____

"Are you going to take your horn in?"

"No way! If we do that, they'll drag us up there."

I chuckled nervously to myself and felt shivers go up and down my spine and stretch through my arms and legs. Part of it was the chilly night breeze coming off the Milwaukee River, some of it was Doug's incredulous tone of voice, but most of it was the thought of taking my trumpet up to the stand and playing it at a nightclub.

The day before, Doug had told me of the blues jams at Dr. Dee's Jazz Riverboat where the blues band playing would let players from the audience (with talents of expected mediocrity) get up and "stretch out" a bit, or in layman's terms, play a couple of choruses. (Student writer)

1. What is this writer writing about? _____

   _____ _____ _____

   _____ _____

2. Why is this writer writing about this? _____

   _____ _____ _____

   _____ _____

Many students in American public schools have writing and reading difficulties, and they are taught a lot of facts that are forgotten because they are not used. These students have become victims of lowered standards in the public school system, but not all schools have suffered because of these lowered standards. The best environment for learning is what we have today in private schools. Here the schools are able to keep manageable class sizes and, because of enforced discipline, a safe environment where students can concentrate on learning instead of racial riots and crime. (Student writer)

1. What is this writer writing about? _____

_____

_____

2. Why is this writer writing about this? _____

_____

_____

    The door opened and I stepped off the bus. Another day of school had gone by as usual. I held the books from my classes wrapped in my arms. As I walked up the driveway, I was met by my dog. She always knew what bus I was on and never failed to meet me. My aunt's car was parked at the top of the driveway. As I walked into the house, I could hear their voices but once my presence was known, their voices died immediately. I said hello as I prepared myself an after school snack, hoping that I didn't have to go in and be polite to my aunt. Abruptly, my aunt announced that she must be getting home. I suddenly had the embarrassed feeling that I had chased her away. Were my mother's eyes red? This whole situation seemed strange.
    "Cindy, I need to talk to you," said my mother.
    Yes, her eyes were swollen and red. I wondered why. She was telling me something, it was important, and her voice had a strange tight tone. But I couldn't be hearing her right because I thought she had just said that my dad was dead, killed in an accident this morning. (Student writer)

1. What is this writer writing about? _____

_____

_____

2. Why is this writer writing about this? _____

_____

_____

The role of the family in America is changing. In the past, life revolved around the family unit. Home was commonly a major source of education, companionship, and security for many individuals, yet today that role seems to be changing. Home is becoming merely a place where family members gather to sleep before leaving again to carry out the following day's agenda. It is becoming noticeably more unusual for the family to serve as the central focus of daily life in our country. Sociologists and social historians, looking for causes, attribute this to changes brought about by the industrial revolution and then the urbanization that followed in its wake. (Student writer)

1. What is this writer writing about? _____

   _____

   _____

2. Why is this writer writing about this? _____

   _____

   _____

Exercise 3

In the previous exercises in this chapter, you've formed clusters by examining either a body of material that you've generated through planning or that has been included in the book for your use. Select one set of clusters from among these to use as the basis for a paper. Then, formulate two preliminary hypotheses about your material that state a purpose for writing.

1. Which set of clusters did you choose? _____

   _____

2. What is your attitude toward the material? _____

   _____

   _____

3. What are two preliminary hypotheses that you could prove by writing about this topic?

a. _____

_____

_____

b. _____

_____

_____

Composing a Discovery Draft

Exercise 1

Respond to one of the situations described below. Using what you have learned about planning and making a scratch outline, write a first discovery draft of your response. When you have finished your discovery draft, answer the questions that follow.

Situation 1: In your college newspaper there is an angry editorial by a member of the newspaper's editorial board. The editorial attacks one of your favorite teachers this semester because he has indicated that he will flunk a student in one of his classes whom he has caught cheating. You are in another class taught by this teacher, and you remember that at the beginning of the semester he clearly announced what he would do about cheating. Since you don't think the teacher should be criticized so harshly for his views, you intend to write a response indicating that the editorial is unfair to the teacher and wrong in not demanding strong action against cheating.

Situation 2: Several days ago as you were walking to class, someone on a bike ran into a pedestrian. The biker immediately got angry at the pedestrian and shouted that she should have gotten out of his way. Though the girl didn't seem to have been hurt, she looked shaken and scared. You are beginning to realize that some of the bikers in the area are becoming a menace because they don't obey traffic rules and seem to think they always have the right of way. Write a letter to the student newspaper calling attention to the problem.

Situation 3: You have just heard that a friend in another part of the state has been hospitalized for over a week. Her doctors have not yet diagnosed her illness, despite extensive testing. Since you know she would appreciate a letter, you are determined to write and feel that you should try to maintain a light, pleasant tone. Write a letter focusing on some of the positive things that have been happening to you lately.

1. To what degree are you satisfied or dissatisfied with this draft? _____

   _____

   _____

   _____

2. What questions do you have about this draft? _____

   _____

   _____

   _____

3. What suggestions do you have for what you need to do next? _____

   _____

   _____

   _____

Exercise 2

In the early draft of the student essay included here, the author's preliminary hypothesis was that he wanted to convince motorcyclists that wearing safety helmets should be mandatory. Read the draft and then answer the questions that follow it.

> About two years ago, I received word that a very close friend of mine had just died in a motorcycle accident. Now just like anyone else, I realize that accidents do happen, but the sad part is that this accidental death could have been prevented. The doctors stated that Tim would have lived had he been wearing a safety helmet.
>
> If Tim's accident would have happened four years ago, he would probably be alive today. You see, four years ago, safety helmets were required

in this state. It was also about four years ago that public pressure led to the repeal of our state's mandatory helmet laws. I personally feel the helmet laws were practical and saved lives. In fact, many people who oppose the helmet laws would probably feel different if they, like me, had lost a very close friend because he was not wearing a safety helmet. I could continue with my personal belief about how much the helmet laws are needed, but instead, let's examine the actual statistics and arguments on both sides of the issue.

Those who oppose the mandatory helmet laws do so for a small number of reasons. First, many riders feel the helmets are an inconvenience and very uncomfortable. Next, some riders feel that the helmets cost too much to be worth buying. The third and most important argument is the idea that the helmet laws are a violation of the people's right to freedom of choice.

To these arguments come the replies from important people like Ben Kelley. Kelley, the Vice-President of the Insurance Institute for Highway Safety, emphasizes that the mandatory helmet laws have already proven to be effective in reducing the death rate of riders by over 30% and the number of serious injuries by over 50%. When Kelley was asked if it is the American way to require riders to wear helmets, he said that if it is not the American way, then neither is requiring milk to be pasteurized, houses to have safety fuses, boaters to wear life jackets, or cars to drive on the right side of the road. What Kelley meant is that throughout America, the promotion of safety is occurring. If it is all right for every other area, why not promote safety among motorcyclists? Kelley also had some interesting statistics. The statistics showed that over 95% of the riders wore helmets when the laws were in effect. They also showed a death rate of about 35% less when the riders were wearing helmets. The facts before, during, and after the mandatory helmet laws all show one thing. Safety helmets do save lives.

In summary, the only real argument against helmet laws is the issue of freedom of choice, and if this argument were to be valid, then our whole system of safety standards is wrong. I personally do not think the United States' standards are too high or too low. The one other argument I would like to comment on is the idea that helmets cost too much. Does a helmet really cost too much?

The average helmet costs between $30 and $130. I personally hope people value life at more than $130 dollars. It is also strange how people change their minds about helmet laws after an accident occurs. I really think people would not think a helmet costs too much if it could save a life. Finally, before you, the motorcycle rider, or you, the friend of a rider, decide whether the mandatory helmet laws are needed, examine the facts. If this is not enough, maybe you should ask some people who almost died in a motorcycle accident whether they think such laws should be in effect. I think their vote would be unanimous, and so should yours. (Student writer)

1. To what degree do you think this draft is satisfactory or unsatisfactory?

   _____

   _____

2. What suggestions do you have to give the writer for what to do next?

   _____

   _____

   _____

   _____

Exercise 3

Using one of the hypotheses you selected in Exercise 3 under "Defining a Preliminary Hypothesis," write a discovery draft of a paper. When you have finished, describe your reaction to the draft by answering the following questions:

1. To what degree are you satisfied or dissatisfied with this draft? _____

   _____

   _____

   _____

2. What questions do you have about this draft? _____

   _____

_____

_____

3. What suggestions do you have for what you need to do next? _____

_____

_____

Constructing a Descriptive Outline

In order to construct a descriptive outline that will help you see how to improve a discovery draft, you need a strategy to describe that draft. One way is to examine your draft paragraph by paragraph to see what each one says (what the topic is) and what it does (how the paragraph is developed and how it functions in the essay). To practice describing what paragraphs say and do, try the following exercises.

Exercise 1

For practice in identifying what paragraphs say and do, read the following three paragraphs and state the topic of each and how it is developed.

> Making a film is very much like building a house, and the script is like an architect's blue-print. The first rudimentary sketches, like the architect's original drawings, give us an impression of what the finished product is intended to look like. This is the story outline. The next step is to make a structural framework. Like the architect's ground plans and elevations, it is a schematic reduction of the material subjected to the stresses it will have to bear. This is what we call the treatment, from which we now proceed to the screenplay proper. The writing of a screenplay requires the continuous interaction of analytical and creative processes: breakdown and build-up. Once the idea has been given shape and substance, it is broken down into its component parts; these parts are individually tested and developed and finally reassembled into the finished product. Sometimes there follows one further stage which in recent years . . . has gradually fallen into abeyance. This is the shooting script, expanding the screenplay into a detailed description of individual camera angles, and providing the director with a carefully worked out plan for shooting the film. (Wolf Rilla, *The Writer and the Screen*)

This paragraph says: _____

_____

_____

This paragraph does: _____

_____

_____

The thing about Little Rock is that it was where television reporting came to influence, if not maturity. As in the case of the Vietnam war a decade later, things might have been very different if it weren't for the new impact of television news: you could not hide from it. In the 1850's a British detachment might fight a desperate battle at the Khyber Pass and a week later the London papers would have an account; it probably takes that kind of delay and the filtering of the blood and smell through a writing reporter to make imperialism possible. Even World War I, where the still camera came of age, went largely unseen until Laurence Stallings published *The First World War*, a book of photographs, in the 1930's. *Life* magazine covered World War II in great and sometimes grisly detail, but it took television to show you the war in Vietnam relentlessly every night to force a democracy to finally make a democratic decision about a war—a democratic decision in which the citizens themselves made up their minds on something very like first-hand evidence. (Harry Reasoner, *Before the Colors Fade*)

This paragraph says: _____

_____

_____

This paragraph does: _____

_____

_____

Six persons in Boston—three males, three females—were recently asked what they would do if notified that the world was going to end in four days. Why four days instead of the more conventionally apocalyptic three we leave as a mystery forever embedded in the mind of the Boston *Herald* reporter who asked the question. It is not the question that startles us but the answers. Two of the women said they would go to Bermuda. One woman answered that she would move up the date of her wedding, which is at present scheduled for December 24th. One man, a law-school student, thought he would take his wife on as long a trip as they could manage in so cruelly curtailed a period. "I'd see America first," he said. So, if these six were a fair cross-section, in the last agony of the United States the highways will be clogged with determined sightseers, the telephone wires jammed with the details of hastily rearranged weddings, and the reservations to Bermuda booked solid. (John Updike, "Doomsday, Mass.," *Assorted Prose*)

This paragraph says: _____

_____

_____

This paragraph does: _____

_____

_____

Write a descriptive outline of the discovery draft you wrote for Exercise 3 under "Composing a Discovery Draft." When you are done, examine this outline and then list what you need to do next. In your list include the major problems that you see and propose some solutions to these problems.

Descriptive outline: _____

_____

_____

_____

_____

_____

_____

_____

_____

_____

_____

Conclusions: _____

_____

_____

_____

_____

_____

_____

_____

_____

_____

_____

COMPOSING AN EFFECTIVE THESIS

Exercise 1

Write a thesis statement for each of the three paragraphs you read in Exercise 1 of "Constructing a Descriptive Outline."

Paragraph 1 (on screenwriting): _____

_____

_____

Paragraph 2 (on TV's depiction of war): _____

_____

_____

Paragraph 3 (on people's reactions to the end of the world): _____

_____

_____

Exercise 2

Examine the following thesis statements, written by students for three-
to four-page papers. Are they sufficiently restricted (appropriately limited
in scope), unified (only one idea expressed), and precise (only one interpretation possible)?

1. There are definite changes that have taken place over the last two
   decades regarding the role that women play in marriage and in the
   family.
   a. What problems do you see with this thesis statement?

   _____

   _____

   _____

   _____

   b. What suggestions for revision can you offer? _____

   _____

   _____

   _____

2. Instituting capital punishment would help our societies in many ways as we would be better off without the killers around.

   a. Problems _____

   _____

   _____

   _____

   b. Suggestions for revision _____

   _____

   _____

   _____

3. Americans do not realize how much we depend on imported oil.

   a. Problems _____

   _____

   _____

   _____

   b. Suggestions for revision _____

   _____

   _____

   _____

4. Gun control is not a very effective method for curtailing crime.

   a. Problems _____

   _____

   _____

   _____

b. Suggestions for revision _____

_____

_____

_____

5. The real problem with grade inflation is in defining what is average and how it should be handled.

a. Problems _____

_____

_____

_____

b. Suggestions for revision _____

_____

_____

_____

6. Our public school system is in deep trouble because of the open, liberal approaches used in the last few decades.

a. Problems _____

_____

_____

_____

b. Suggestions for revision _____

_____

_____

_____

7. Among college students alcoholism in the dorms is one of the hottest issues around.

   a. Problems _____

   _____

   _____

   _____

   b. Suggestions for revision _____

   _____

   _____

   _____

8. A new, more modern sports arena is not an extravagance for this college but a necessity.

   a. Problems _____

   _____

   _____

   _____

   b. Suggestions for revision _____

   _____

   _____

   _____

9. Living primitively for ten days in the wilderness made me realize how much I enjoyed the serenity and simplicity nature possesses and how much I wanted to contain it inside myself.

   a. Problems _____

   _____

_____

_____

b. Suggestions for revision _____

_____

_____

_____

10. Professional football overemphasizes a few stars instead of promoting team effort the way basketball does.

a. Problems _____

_____

_____

_____

b. Suggestions for revision _____

_____

_____

_____

Exercise 3

Practice formulating thesis statements by writing a possible thesis statement for a three- to four-page paper for each of the topics listed here:

1. Entrance exams for college

_____

_____

_____

2. The value of afterschool jobs in high school

_____

_____

_____

3. Final exams

_____

_____

_____

4. Using "PG," "R," and "X" to rate movies

_____

_____

_____

5. The importance of being able to communicate effectively

_____

_____

_____

CONSTRUCTING A FORMAL OUTLINE

Read the following essay about where people get most of their news and then construct a formal outline of the essay. Test your outline according to the criteria listed below.

WHERE DO YOU GET YOUR NEWS?

The idea that most Americans get most of their news from television has for some time been regarded as both true and alarming. With noble earnestness, Walter Cronkite used to plead that his half-hour script would not fill three-quarters of a single newspaper page and that distortion was "the inevitable result of trying to get ten pounds of news into the one-pound sack we are given each night." Speaking at a du Pont Awards ceremony at Columbia University in February, NBC's Tom Brokaw said that unfortunately many Americans "have come to rely on us as their primary and only source of information" and "we are inadequate to that task." It just may be the anchormen should relax a little.

In a special news-media issue of the *Wilson Quarterly*, Professor Lawrence W. Lichty at the University of Maryland challenges the idea that TV news is so dominant. Judging the argument involves assessing the nitpicking of several interested parties. Back in 1959 the Roper Organization, commissioned by the television industry, began asking this question, repeating it every two years: "Where do you usually get most of your news about what's going on in the world today"? The last time, in 1980, 64% cited TV, 44% newspapers, 18% radio, 5% magazines and 4% "talking to people." But that adds up to 135%! Well, multiple answers were permitted. A Roper spokesman says that "whatever the deficiencies" of the question, repeating it the same way each time provides a consistent pattern. Yes, but why can't Roper ask, "Well, which is it—do you get *most* of your news from TV or from the papers?" That would be forcing an answer and lead to impure results, says the Television Information Office, which hires Roper. Leo Bogart, a sociologist who heads the Newspaper Advertising Bureau, agrees that Roper measures the public's "perception" of where it gets the news, even if the public is wrong.

Professor Lichty takes the common-sense view that most people get their news from many sources. He marshals some competing statistics from Simmons Market Research, which print people pay for: 68% of U.S. adults read at least part of some newspaper every day. ("At least part" is another of those suspicious phrases.) Less than a third of U.S. adults watch TV news, local or national, on a given day—a figure Simmons says may be too low. And 31% of adults read one of the three newsmagazines, *Time, Newsweek* and *U.S. News & World Report*.

Still, "perceptions" of TV dominance, erroneous or not, do have consequences. Bogart thinks it wrong for newspapers, particularly declining ones, to copy television's emphasis on personalities and features, to cut news items to car-radio brevity, or to favor routine "chicken dinner" local coverage. Major stories of national and international importance, he argues, have most impact on newspaper readers.

Newsgatherers at the networks despise much local TV news, and CBS's Dan Rather has had the temerity to say so. In the *Wall Street Journal* he noted that local stations have increased their news programming by 300%. "The real problem," Rather wrote, "is not too much news. It's too much chatter masquerading as news." Amen to that. Rather concluded, "But most Americans still rely on the network evening newscast for their information." Wrong perception, Dan.

As Professor Lichty puts it, "The widely accepted notion that Mr.

Rather and his rivals each command a vast, devoted nightly following
seems farfetched." Together the nightly newscasts on the three networks
gather an audience of 50 million. It is a sizable number, even when split
three ways, but does not add up to "most Americans." Besides, Lichty
says, it is a fickle and fluctuating audience: "Only 1% of all 78.3 million
American television households watch Rather as often as four or five
nights a week." The Television Information Office disputes these figures,
and counters with a Nielsen report that 4.2% of all TV homes watch
Rather four or five times a week, not that much more impressive.

From all this stunting with statistics, two conclusions can be drawn.
It is good that the networks are more serious than the local chatterers.
But it is nice to learn that those golden network anchormen are not such
awesome, dominating influences over us after all. (Thomas Griffith,
"Where Do You Get Your News?" *Time*)

Formal Outline

_____

_____

_____

_____

_____

_____

_____

_____

_____

_____

_____

_____

_____

_____

_____

_____

Testing the Outline

1. Is the thesis satisfactory? _____

_____

_____

2. Are the relationships among the parts clear and consistent? _____

_____

_____

3. Does the order of the parts provide a logical progression? _____

_____

_____

4. Is the outline complete? _____

_____

_____

5. Is each entry developed in detail? _____

_____

_____

4
Revising

LOOKING TO REVISE

To gather different perspectives on your writing and to see how readers' reactions differ, ask three people who are not in your class to comment on a draft of something you have written for this class or as part of an exercise in this book. If nothing is readily available, write an answer to one of the following questions:

1. Is there such a thing as school spirit? Why?
2. If the current President of the United States were running again for election, would you vote for him? Why?
3. Do you think that racial discrimination is still a major problem in our society? Why?
4. Assume that you were given tickets to your favorite athletic event and also to a really fabulous concert. They will both take place at the same time. Which one would you choose to attend? Why?
5. Describe the most annoying habit of one of your friends or acquaintances.
6. If you won a week's vacation somewhere (all expenses paid), where would you go? Why?
7. If you were making a New Year's resolution to change something about yourself or about the conditions around you, what would that resolution be? Why?
8. Should there be military training on college campuses? Why?
9. What is the best thing that has happened to you during the last year?
10. Do you think that older students who have returned to school have special problems?

Give your writing to three different people and ask them to react. Record their reactions here:

1. _____

_____

_____

_____

_____

_____

2. _____

_____

_____

_____

_____

3. _____

_____

_____

_____

_____

If there are similarities between the comments, what are they?

_____

_____

_____

_____

What are some of the differences between the comments?

_____

_____

_____

_____

Can you categorize the comments in any way? For example, are some of the comments evaluations (such as "I liked the first part"); are there some general impressions of the larger elements of your writing (such as "The subject is an interesting one"); are there comments about specific problems (such as "You need a comma here"); or are there different categories?

Categories:

_____

_____

_____

_____

_____

_____

_____

_____

_____

_____

READING TO REVISE

Reading for Subject

Exercise 1

To practice deciding which subjects attract and sustain your attention, browse through a magazine that has a variety of subjects, such as *Time*, *Newsweek*, *Scientific American*, or *Harper's*. Write down the first ten subjects you see and very quickly comment on the degree to which they interest you. Then, look at five subjects (taken from the magazine *Psychology Today*) and comment on the degree to which these subjects interest you.

	Subject	How interesting is this subject?
1.	_____	
	_____	_____
2.	_____	
	_____	_____
3.	_____	
	_____	_____
4.	_____	
	_____	_____
5.	_____	
	_____	_____
6.	_____	
	_____	_____
7.	_____	

_____   _____

8. _____

_____   _____

9. _____

_____   _____

10. _____

_____   _____

11. Recent findings on household chemicals that can endanger people's nervous systems   _____

12. Characteristics of people who are able to withstand the isolation of wintering in the Antarctic   _____

13. Some unconscious reasons for smoking   _____

14. The need for offering support to victims of crime   _____

15. "Burn-out" among teachers   _____

If possible, exchange books with a classmate and offer your comments on the first ten subjects in that person's book. Then, compare your answers for the last five subjects.

In general, did you both tend to agree or disagree?

_____

Would you say that the other writer does or does not share your interests?

_____

Exercise 2

To practice reading for the subject of an essay, in preparation for revision, read the following excerpts from student and professional essays.

For each excerpt, answer the questions that follow the writing.

There is probably nothing more bewildering than the profusion of options and variations facing the first time computer buyer. How many people become interested in computers after reading about a $1000 business computer, only to be quoted $5000 (or more) for the computer that fits their application? It would appear that even automobile salesmen could learn from computer salesmen when it comes to adding a lot of options that pump up the purchase price. With an automobile you probably understand what each option is; if you find yourself paying 50% more than you intended for a new car, you may feel that you got talked into something, but at least you understand what you were talked into. On the other hand, when you discover that the computer suited to your needs costs three or four times as much as you thought it would, you may well feel confused and uncomprehending (Adam Osborne and Steven Cook, *Business System Buyer's Guide)*

1. What is the subject of this paragraph? _____

_____

2. Is there only one subject or does the excerpt suggest that the rest of

the writing may have more than one subject?_____

_____

3. Does the excerpt get to the subject directly or is there a prolonged

digression?_____

_____

4. What, in your opinion, is significant about the subject? _____

_____

5. What, in your opinion, is interesting about the subject? _____

_____

6. As a reader, would you read the rest of this writing? Why? _____

_____

Five key factors used to assess the power of a country are 1) its critical mass, which is the population of the country plus the amount of territory that country covers; 2) its economic capability to withstand the effects of a war; 3) its military capability; 4) its strategic purpose, which takes into account how well its men are trained and how competent its officers are; and 5) its national will to win and to back the war. Using these factors, I plan to compare the United States of America to the U.S.S.R., along with other countries. I do not think we are prepared for a war. The U.S.A. and the U.S.S.R. are the two super powers of the world. They could, in less than thirty minutes, destroy all of the cities and most of the people in each country. The people who would survive such a nuclear war would most likely have radiation burns of some kind or another. (Student writer)

1. What is the subject of this paragraph? _____

_____

2. Is there only one subject or does the excerpt suggest that the rest of

the writing may have more than one subject? _____

_____

3. Does the excerpt get to the subject directly or is there a prolonged

digression? _____

_____

4. What, in your opinion, is significant about the subject? _____

_____

5. What, in your opinion, is interesting about the subject? _____

_____

6. As a reader, would you continue to read the rest of this writing? Why?

_____

_____

OF ORGANIC CHICKENS AND HAPPY EGGS

The health-food industry and its gurus have fostered the fashion and fear in every conceivable way. Power of suggestion is amply put to work. Advertisements and placards in the stores greet us with, "Do you feel tired, run-down. . .?" If you've just come from a hard day at the office or are escaping from a houseful of young children (even one child, if toddler age, may qualify as a houseful), the answer is probably, "Yes." (Or, "Yes!!") Another favorite is: "Do you have minor aches and pains you didn't used to have?" Well, if we think about it hard enough, most of us can conjure up a twinge or two we hadn't noticed yesterday. Some alfalfa meal will fix us right up, we're advised, along with a big bottle of vitamin E and some desiccated liver. (Dr. Elizabeth M. Whelan and Dr. Fredrick J. Stare, *The One-Hundred-Percent Natural, Purely Organic, Cholesterol-Free, Magavitamin, Low-Carbohydrate Nutrition Hoax*)

1. What is the subject of this paragraph? _____

_____

2. Is there only one subject or does the excerpt suggest that the rest of

the writing may have more than one subject? _____

_____

3. Does the excerpt get to the subject directly or is there a prolonged

digression? _____

_____

4. What, in your opinion, is significant about the subject? _____

_____

5. What, in your opinion, is interesting about the subject? _____

_____

6. As a reader, would you continue to read the rest of this writing? Why?

_____

_____

Exercise 3

Select an early draft of a paper you've written either for earlier exercises in this book, for your class, or for some other writing task. Read this paper just as you read the excerpts above and answer the same questions.

1. What is the subject of this writing? _____

   _____

2. Is there only one subject or does the excerpt suggest that the rest of

   the writing may have more than one subject? _____

   _____

3. Does the excerpt get to the subject directly or is there a prolonged

   digression? _____

   _____

4. What, in your opinion, is significant about the subject? _____

   _____

5. What, in your opinion, is interesting about the subject? _____

   _____

6. As a reader, would you continue to read the rest of this writing? Why?

   _____

   _____

Reading for Audience

Exercise 1

To practice reading your writing for possible audience problems, compare the degree to which the writers of the following excerpts on gun control have considered their audiences. After you read both introductory excerpts, answer the questions that follow.

WE NEED GUNS

The arguments regarding whether we have the right to own a gun have been long and drawn out. Many people feel that guns threaten our livelihood and should, therefore, be controlled. But these people don't realize the consequences that would occur if we were not able to bear arms. Americans should keep this right to be able to own a gun.

Guns are dangerous. There is no way around that fact. A good criminal is not complete without one. Countless people are killed innocently every year by them. But the story doesn't stop there. Guns are also invaluable as a form of protection. Crimes would not slow down if guns were controlled. In fact, taking guns away would be a poor deterrent. Taking away guns takes away from the law-abiding citizen his own form of protection. This limits a man's defense of self, family, and home. The police cannot be everywhere at once. All they can do is try to catch the criminal after the fact. If one has to call the police, they won't have the time to get there to save the innocent people. A handgun is the best means of self-defense, and owning a gun is completely all right. (Student writer)

NO GUN CONTROL

"A well-regulated militia, being necessary to the security of a free State, the right of the people to keep and bear arms, shall not be infringed." This is how the Second Amendment reads. "A well-regulated militia" has been interpreted by the Supreme Court to mean that any U.S. citizen armed with a pistol or rifle constitutes the reserve militia force of the United States.

Let us examine first the reasons our founding fathers felt it was necessary to bear arms, and second, what will happen if liberal idealists are allowed to invoke gun control laws upon a law-abiding oppressed majority.

Defense of self, family, and home is a natural and permanent right. Government does not give this right and cannot take it away, but it is an enduring temptation of government to tamper with it. It is not reasonable that one be denied weapons appropriate to his condition, to his civilization, and to those conditions he might face in the hands of men who murder, rape, and destroy. It is not that we should depend for our right to be armed upon a constitutional provision. No man, nor any group of men, should, or has a right to, pass judgment as to whether one should have, in peaceable possession in his home, the means for keeping its precincts secure and sacred. This is the natural thing. It is the permanent thing. (Student writer)

1. Describe some of the values, assumptions, and prejudices of the people whom these writers expect to be their audience. To what extent are the audiences similar in these two excerpts and to what degree are they different?

_____

_____

_____

_____

_____

2. How would a member of the National Rifle Association or anyone else who opposes gun-control legislation react to these two excerpts?

_____

_____

_____

_____

_____

3. How would someone who supports legislation to register and control guns react to each of these writings?

_____

_____

_____

_____

_____

4. Compare the degrees to which these two writers acknowledge the perspective of people whose viewpoint differs from their own.

_____

_____

_____

_____

_____

_____

Exercise 2

The writers of the following excerpts expect a certain kind of audience for their writing. Describe that audience by answering the questions following each excerpt.

> After a prolonged fall from investor favor, biotechnology is back in vogue on Wall Street. Although this fledgling industry is years away from generating sizable earnings, prices of most biotechnology stocks have at least doubled in the stock market rally that began last August. And investors' keen appetite for speculative new issues is triggering another round of initial offerings by biotech companies.
>
> Last to come to market is Biogen, the last of the major privately held biotechnology companies, which sold its first shares to the public on Mar. 22. The Cambridge (Mass.) company lost $4.5 million on revenues of $20.6 million in 1982. But Biogen's 2.5 million-share initial offering was quickly snapped up at $23 a share and closed its first day of trading slightly higher. (*Business Week*, April 4, 1983)

1. Describe the values, assumptions, and prejudices of the appropriate

audience for this excerpt. _____

_____

_____

_____

2. What specialized interests should the audience for this paper have?

_____

_____

_____

_____

3. Describe the expected audience, in terms of age, type of job, level of education, income, and so on. _____

_____

_____

_____

> Though some people persist in comparing loudspeakers by the size (or number) of their drivers, we've often said that such yardsticks are meaningless indicators of sound quality. Can you predict the low-frequency output of a system on the basis of its woofer's diameter or magnet weight? Of course not. We've heard some pretty miserable-sounding loudspeakers that should've sounded great if those were important factors. So rather than detail those "specifications" here, we will be providing such information as sensitivity (efficiency), cabinet size, and price—all of which should prove far more useful in determining whether a speaker will complement your system and listening room. And though it hardly needs restating, the ultimate criterion is the sound. (Peter Dobbin, "Speakers," *High Fidelity*)

1. Describe the values, assumptions, and prejudices of the appropriate audience for this excerpt. _____

_____

_____

_____

2. What specialized interests should the audience for this paper have?

_____

_____

_____

_____

3. Describe the expected audience in terms of age, type of job, level of

   education, income, and so on. _____

_____

_____

_____

A fine old agricultural institution, the windshield crop survey, may be fading from the scene. More and more farmers are deciding that to really keep tabs on a crop, the only thing they want between themselves and the plants is a hand lens, not a windshield.

Entomologist Steve Moore of the University of Illinois thinks farmers' efforts to keep a closer watch on crops and pests—either by scouting fields themselves or by hiring a professional—are showing visible results in the form of reduced losses to pests.

"Because of changing farming practices, we find black cutworms on more acres now than in the past," says Moore. "Yet, when we get calls from farmers, they usually describe the amount of damage as 10% or less. Years ago, by the time we got a call, 20% to 50% of the stand usually had been lost.

"That means somebody is out there looking closely at those fields," says Moore.

1. Describe the values, assumptions, and prejudices of the appropriate

   audience for this excerpt. _____

_____

_____

_____

2. What specialized interests should the audience for this paper have?

_____

_____

_____

3. Describe the expected audience in terms of age, type of job, level of

education, income, and so on. _____

_____

_____

_____

>   For me nothing ever quite equals the pleasure of a visit to the theater,
> and, when it also means a visit to the birthplace of the playwright, I am
> doubly intrigued. When the playwright in question is William Shakespeare
> and the birthplace, Stratford-upon-Avon, I cannot be stopped from book-
> ing seats. Whether comedy, history, or tragedy is to be acted out upon the
> stage of the Royal Shakespeare Theatre, the play is certain to be enjoyed.
>   I like to be slow and old-fashioned when I leave London for Stratford.
> It is quite possible to dash up for a matinee and get back that same day, as
> I once did in my green youth on a very great occasion when I had lunch
> with Sir John Gielgud's mother, a Terry from the famous acting family—
> capped by a backstage meeting afterward with Sir John himself, who had
> just given a sublime performance as Cassius in *Julius Caesar*. I returned to
> London in the late afternoon in a daze of glory. These days I prefer to
> book seats for two plays, stay overnight or longer, and enjoy Shakespeare's
> country as well as the works of that extraordinary poet and playwright.
> This gives me a chance to search out new restaurants, which can be a re-
> warding exercise. (Elisabeth Lambert Ortiz, "Shakespeare's Stratford,"
> *Gourmet*)

1. Describe the values, assumptions, and prejudices of the appropriate

audience for this excerpt. _____

_____

_____

_____

2. What specialized interests should the audience for this paper have?

_____

_____

_____

_____

3. Describe the expected audience in terms of age, type of job, level of

education, income, and so on. _____

_____

_____

_____

Exercise 3

Do the writers of the following excerpts help you focus on the subject and follow the development of the topic? As you read, notice especially the focus and organization of each piece of writing.

At six o'clock in the evening, the plane door opened and we had arrived. We were greeted with a friendly "Hola," and we made our way down a long ramp through a dreary hallway. Finally, we reached a door which led outside. There we were strolling through a tropical jungle paradise full of palm trees, exotic flowers, and colorful birds. Upon reaching the bus, we heard the sound of crashing ocean waves coming up along the shore, and as we rode along, we could see the sunset, a golden ball disappearing into the horizon.

When we approached the hotel, we saw the boutiques and village shops nearby. Our luggage was brought to us, and we all trooped to our rooms to change for dinner. Up in our room we were astonished by the hundreds of lights we could see burning on the mountainside. I thought that Acapulco would be the most beautiful resort area in the world, but as it turned out the next day, it was not all sandy beaches and swaying palms.

Our first day in the city started out with a city bus ride. We stood upon the corner as the ancient, dingy blue and dusty grey hack approached. It rattled to a slow stop. We ascended in single file and placed our pesos in a rusty tin can that the driver held in his calloused hand. The floor was a mess of dirt, sand, and saltwater collecting in the holes

in the linoleum. As we entered the city, the bus came to a shaky halt
near the main markets. We stepped down onto the burning pavement
and made our way across the street. The temperature had already reached
95 degrees.

Across the street were the main markets. Here the natives brought
goods to sell to unsuspecting customers. The shops were all open air,
many with no sides or roofs, and all very small. They displayed their
hand-cut ornaments carved from jade, onyx, and turquoise, most of
which came from Japan. The natives were shrewd businessmen; even
though they came down on their prices, they still had the edge over the
tourists. (Student writer)

1. After you read the first three or four sentences, what did you antici-

   pate as the subject of the rest of the writing? _____

   _____

   _____

2. How does the writer organize the material to help you see where it is

   going next? _____

   _____

3. How does the writer attempt to keep your interest? _____

   _____

Included here is the final paragraph of the essay. After you read it,
answer the questions below.

When evening came, we made our way back to the hotel by way of a
taxi. When we got back, my day's sightseeing made me think how much
first glances can be deceiving. Behind the crystal shores and quiet breezes
of Acapulco lie many hidden images of poverty.

1. Judging from this last paragraph, what do you think the topic of the

   paper was? _____

   _____

2. How well does this match the paper's introductory paragraphs?

_____

_____

The year 1968 was a very important year in the history of the automobile. It was the year the shoulder harness was first required. It was the year of the invention of the catalytic converter. Most importantly, it was the year in which the government became fully involved in regulating the auto industry. The government's reason for all of its rules and regulations was that the American public demanded them. The real reason, however, for government intervention was the media. The media, through visual aids and biased reporting, had convinced the American public that their cars were unsafe and gross polluters. The media's motives for this attack on an American institution, the car, are unclear; however, its effects are staggering.

It is estimated that 45 million people watch television daily, and this figure is still rising. With the power to reach this many people daily, the power of television is unquestioned. By spending enormous amounts of money, politicians have gotten a huge amount of national exposure via the air waves. How a politician looks and comes across on television is more important than what he says. The visual aspects of the media are by far the most powerful. Whether it is a still photograph, film footage, or some unedited piece of on-the-spot reporting, the visual impact is instantaneous and effective. The visual effects of the media and certain government legislation have a direct relationship between them. For example, all the movies and documentaries about the effects of alcohol and driving have led to such laws as the mandatory breath-analysis tests to spot possible drunk drivers. Whether or not the American public drinks too much is not a matter of statistics but one of visual effects. The visual display leaves room for only one conclusion: No one can drink and drive; and since many of us drink, we must protect ourselves from ourselves. (Student writer)

1. After you read the first three or four sentences, what did you anticipate as the subject of the rest of the writing? _____

_____

_____

2. How does the writer organize the material to help you see where it is going next? _____

3. Did the second paragraph continue with the subject that you had

anticipated? _____

_____

Included here is the final paragraph of the essay. After you read it, answer the questions below.

> In conclusion, the rise and fall of the car over the years has been in-fluenced at times by outside sources. The media and the big business owners of the media have influenced the car's long history considerably. Media coverage has led to more government rules and regulations. Though these regulations have cramped the car's performance and styling, they will never detract from the car's colorful past.

1. Judging from this last paragraph, what do you think the topic of the

paper was? _____

_____

2. How well does this match the paper's introductory paragraphs?

_____

_____

Exercise 4

In Exercise 3 under "Reading for Subject," you assessed the need to revise a draft of one of your writings. Read that same draft again to assess the need for revision in terms of audience. The following suggestions and questions can help you make that assessment:

1. Describe the values, assumptions, and prejudices of the audience for your writing.
2. What should the audience already know about your subject?
3. Do you answer possible questions your audience might ask?
4. Does your writing help the audience focus on your topic?
5. Does your organization help the audience to see where the draft is going and to see a logical transition from idea to idea?

Reading for Purpose

Read this early draft of an essay on bicycle safety and then answer the questions that follow.

TWO-WHEELED MANIACS

A pat on the back is in order for the University Police Department. I was wondering how long the students here would be terrorized by bicyclists before some action would be taken. The ten dollar ticketing is a step in the right direction to insure that students may once again walk to classes without fearing for their safety. Bicyclists have not limited their dangerous ways to pedestrians and have caused immense problems for the average automobile driver too. I'm sure many drivers now have hope that someday they may drive down the streets once again and not have to weave to avoid bicyclists.

Those wild and insane bicyclists have been running around bellyaching ever since that first ten dollar fine was assessed, and their cries and pleas have fallen on deaf ears. If only they themselves were not so blind, they could see the hardships they have caused. When will they learn that sidewalks were made for travel on foot, not rubber? When will they learn that our college's beautiful grounds were not manicured with extreme care so that they could make unsightly paths and deep ruts? When will they learn that a red light means stop and a yellow means caution? If they do not learn now, they will learn the hard way, by paying fines and (worse yet) hurting some innocent pedestrians.

It is only a matter of time until a death results from these two-wheeled maniacs. A strict crackdown is the only answer for such a problem. Right now, only bicyclists have rights. Motorists and pedestrians have to yield and always pay the consequences. This situation must stop. We cannot walk the sidewalks in fear of bikers. The University Police has my support in their new campaign for bicycle safety and deserves your support as well. (Student writer)

1. What do you think the writer's purpose is? _____

   _____

2. What is the thesis of the essay? _____

   _____

3. Does the body of the essay fulfill the promise of the thesis? _____

If not, what part of the promise is not fulfilled? _____

_____

4. Is every part of the essay sufficiently developed? _____

_____

Included here is a revision of the essay "Two-Wheeled Maniacs." Read it and answer the questions that follow.

SOLVING THE PROBLEM

Riding bicycles is a privilege that we Americans have, and it is a privilege that has often been abused. The fault for these abuses does not always fall on the bicyclist himself, but may instead fall on the pedestrian, motorist, or society as a whole. There are not any simple solutions to this problem, but implementation of a few changes in policy could mean safer travel for all concerned.

The first place to start in cleaning up bicycle problems concerns our local police agencies. The registration and licensing of bicycles would benefit all concerned. By paying a small fee for this service, the bikers would indeed have a right to use public streets. Policemen would be able to track down offenders and thus protect the innocent by virtue of their registration. This service would also be helpful in finding stolen bicycles, which is becoming commonplace. The nominal fee would pay for the time and effort of this service and not burden non-bicycle-riding tax payers. Along with the annual check of license, a quick safety check of brakes, lights, and horns would also be in order. It is not too much to ask a biker to be able to stop quickly, be seen at night, and be able to sound a warning.

Once the bicyclist has a safe piece of equipment and has been registered, he is legally ready to take to the streets—or is he? He should now be instructed concerning the laws and rules of the road. A simple brochure should inform him of all the traffic laws and the penalties for breaking those laws.

Even with this accomplished, the task of bicycle safety is not yet completed as the pedestrian and the motorist must observe safety rules too. Since cars and bikes should not use the sidewalks, pedestrians should not use the streets. If pedestrians use crosswalks and refrain from stepping out in front of bikers, this would go a long way toward solving the problem.

And the motorist should not consider the bikers as enemies, but should allow them to use the streets as they rightly ought to. This mutual respect between biker, motorist, and pedestrian may be the hardest to achieve, but it will undoubtedly be the most important.

The friction that now occurs between motorists, bicyclists, and pedestrians will not be easy to stop, but it is not impossible and the effort must be made to do it. An effort will have to be made and will have to involve mutual respect between all. The initial steps can be taken by the police, and should include licensing, registration, safety checks, and instruction on the rules of the road. Bicycles can indeed become a safe transportation system, but only after common sense and respect become evident on all sides.

1. What is the writer's purpose? _____

   _____

2. What is the thesis of the essay? _____

   _____

3. Does the body of the essay fulfill the promise of the thesis? _____

   _____

   If not, what part of the promise is not fulfilled? _____

   _____

4. Is every part of the essay sufficiently developed? _____

   _____

   If not, what needs more development? _____

   _____

5. To what degree is the revision more or less effective than the first

   draft? _____

   Why? _____

   _____

Read the introductions to the following essays and ask yourself what the papers will have to contain, given what the thesis promises. Write as legally binding a contract as possible for the author to sign. State what the writer has promised to offer and what he or she must include in the essay to fulfill this promise.

> The ultimate objective of cults today is to take control of the minds and lives of their members. By abusing our constitutional rights to religious freedom, they are turning responsive, thinking human beings into obedient, unthinking robots. Some may claim that the beliefs and practices of these cults have won converts because of what they offer. There is no doubt that some have joined cults under these circumstances and stayed initially because of an attraction to what the cult offered. But, whether they have come voluntarily or whether they have been lured by false promises, members of cults stay on because of the cults' use of mind technology, more commonly known as "brainwashing." This is their chief tool in attracting and retaining members to their cult. (Student writer)

1. What does this writer promise to offer the reader?

   _____

   _____

   _____

2. To fulfill this promise, what must the writer include in the essay?

   _____

   _____

   _____

> The 80's have been, so far, a difficult time for colleges and universities in America. Decreasing enrollment and dwindling budgets have been the major problem, yet in the midst of these troubles, trade schools are thriving. Scorned by educators as second class institutions, trade schools are registering almost a 25% increase in enrollment each year since 1980. Despite high tuition and imperiled federal aid to these schools, hundreds of thousands of young adults are spurning colleges for training that can

assure them of high-demand careers, a head start in on-the-job experience, and beginning salaries that are often higher than those of college students who graduate with reasonably marketable degrees. (Student writer)

1. What does this writer promise?

    _____

    _____

    _____

    _____

2. To fulfill this promise, what must the writer include in the essay?

    _____

    _____

    _____

    _____

   The art of making up multiple-choice tests is even harder than the art of taking such tests. The test-taker merely has to study, master the material, and then remember it long enough to use it while taking the test. Test-makers, on the other hand, face a difficult task: how to make people miss questions whose subject matter they actually understand. This may sound silly, but it is important and involves limiting the time allowed. Veteran test-takers know, for instance, that the key to doing well on SAT math items lies in finding quick solutions; if you have to perform a complex or lengthy calculation, you've probably missed the trick. The other difficulty that test-makers face is writing questions that are neither misleading nor ambiguous, and this may even be a harder challenge than creating questions which require the test-taker to use a considerable amount of knowledge quickly. (Adapted from David Owen, "1983: The Last Days of ETS," *Harper's*, May 1983)

1. What does this writer promise?

    _____

    _____

_____

2. To fulfill this promise, what must the writer include in the essay?

_____

_____

_____

_____

REVISION AGENDA

Exercise 1

Try to determine the revision agenda of the two versions of the essay on bicycle safety above. To do so, answer the following questions:

1. What did the writer try to do in version 1? _____

_____

_____

_____

What did the writer try to do in version 2? _____

_____

_____

_____

2. What are the strengths and weaknesses of version 1? _____

_____

_____

_____

What are the strengths and weaknesses of version 2? _____

_____

_____

_____

3. What are some of the major revisions made in version 2? _____

_____

_____

_____

Exercise 2

To practice using a revision agenda, look at the draft of a paper you have been working on and answer the questions offered here. After you have answered the questions to your satisfaction, revise the paper so that you incorporate your suggestions.

1. What did you try to do in this draft? _____

_____

_____

_____

2. What are the strengths and weaknesses of this draft? _____

_____

_____

_____

3. What revisions do you want to make in the next draft? _____

5

Common Methods of Development

NARRATION/DESCRIPTION

Recognizing the Strategy

In the selection below, the writer is describing an object. Given the purpose of the description, is it complete or does it need more detail?

THE ALIEN

The other day, a most unusual thing happened. I was walking to my English class when I noticed a very short man in a hooded overcoat. He was beckoning me from behind the armory building. When I approached him, he removed his hood, and needless to say, I was quite startled by his appearance. Obviously, he was not human. He offered me a gnarled left hand (I assumed that it was a hand) in reassurance and began speaking English in an accent which sounded slightly French. He told me that he had overheard one of the younger humans talking about how many screwdrivers he had consumed at a party the night before. He also said that he was very hungry, and he asked me to describe one of these screwdrivers so that he might find one for himself.

Well, I knew my professor would not believe this particular "why I was late today" story, and I also knew that this alien would not be able to find any screwdrivers, unless he happened to wander into a fraternity. However, I decided to help him anyway. He assured me that he had a good command of the English language and could associate with most adjectives and adverbs.

I began by describing its appearance: "A screwdriver is an orange-yellow colored mixture of liquid substances. The first substance is called 'orange juice.' It is the orange-colored liquid which is squeezed out of a certain type of tropical fruit. It has slightly thicker consistency than water and often has pulpy pieces of the fruit floating in it. The second substance is called 'vodka.' It is the liquid product of fermented potatoes and water. It is colorless, like water, and has very nearly the same consistency. The mixture of these two substances is often found in a round, open-topped, twelve-ounce container made of clear glass. Usually, there are also some grey-white cubes of frozen water floating on the surface of the liquid. Often there is a long, thin, plastic device known as a 'swizzle stick' dipped in the substance."

I then proceeded to describe the taste and smell: "The substance called a screwdriver has a very pungent odor. I am assuming that little thing in the middle of your face can smell." He assured me that it could. I continued: "The smell is primarily a tangy smell from the orange juice, but the pure, strong, medicine-like smell of the vodka also comes through. The taste is a most enjoyable blend of the tart, tangy, freshness of the orange juice and the strong, clean, smoothness of the vodka."

I finished my description with: "There is one unusual quality of this particular substance called a screwdriver. It has quite a unique effect on the being who consumes mass quantities of them. He becomes dizzy, has severely decreased muscle coordination, tells jokes that are not measurably humorous, and occasionally regurgitates the substance completely. My advice to you is to consume no more than two full containers of the substance."

My description completed, the alien smiled (I think it was a smile) and expressed his gratitude. He turned around and walked away with bounding steps. I experienced a twinge of conscience that told me I should have directed him to some better form of sustenance. But then I formed a mental picture of this alien drunk on screwdrivers and swaying as he walked, and I laughed out loud all the way to my English class. (Jim Jozwiak, student writer)

a. What is the purpose of describing the object? _____

_____

b. Given this purpose, is the description complete? _____ If not, what

more is needed? _____

_____

c. Could anything in the description or narrative of events be eliminated?

_____ If so, what? _____

_____

d. List several of the most effective details in the description and explain briefly why they are effective.

_____

_____

_____

In the next selection the writer is describing a person. Given the purpose of the description, is it complete or is more detail needed?

SERGEANT JONES

I stepped off the big blue Air Force Bus into the cool Texas night. Standing in a loose, sloppy formation among the men I had arrived with from the San Antonio airport, I nervously studied my surroundings. We were standing on a large walkway in front of a big brown building. Hanging above the doorway was a large sign that read: "Welcome to Lackland Air Force Base." As I was studying this sign, the door below it slowly opened and in the doorway stood one of the biggest and meanest looking men I had ever seen! This towering hulk was to be my drill sergeant for the next six weeks of basic training. His name was Sergeant Jones.

Sergeant Jones stood about 6'5" and weighed in at around 240 lbs. He always wore the standard drill sergeant campaign (Smokey the Bear) hat which made him look even taller. He had short blond regulation hair and a neatly trimmed Hitler-style mustache. His eyes were a piercing dark blue which would send shivers up your spine if directed toward you. His nose was large with a small bump about half-way down which was probably caused from a break that happened earlier in his life. His mouth always bore a sarcastic smirk, sometimes revealing his large straight teeth, yellowed from years of smoking cigarettes. His chin protruded out further than the average man's and had a small scar on the right side which added to his mean look.

His neck was thick and led to very broad shoulders and a large chest which filled out his fatigue shirt. His five stripes were perfectly aligned on each sleeve with a perfect crease right through the middle. His pants, with a shiny new belt buckle, were also carefully creased and just barely touched his spit-shined combat boots. From head to toe he was regulation perfect. He would make a great recruiting poster! (Randy Rinehart, student writer)

a. What is the writer's purpose in describing this person? _____

_____

b. How do the details contribute to achieving the writer's purpose?

_____

_____

_____

c. Should anything be added to or eliminated from this essay? _____

_____

d. List several of the most effective details and explain briefly why they

are effective. _____

_____

_____

Practicing the Strategy

Select two of the topics below and list four or five details that could be included in a paragraph on that topic.

1. With pen and paper in hand, go to a restaurant, cafeteria, or fast-food establishment and list some of the details that would describe that particular place.

_____

_____

_____

_____

_____

2. Describe a character on TV whom you especially like or dislike.

_____

_____

_____

_____

_____

3. Narrate a pleasant event in your past. This could be something that happened on a vacation or a personal victory or happy occurrence in your family.

_____

_____

_____

_____

_____

4. Describe an event that you attended that may be unfamiliar to other readers, for example a rodeo, a farm show, a demolition derby, an outdoor concert, a mime show, or an Olympic competition.

_____

_____

_____

_____

_____

5. Like the writer of "The Alien," describe a common, everyday object to an extraterrestrial being who has no previous knowledge of such an object.

_____

_____

_____

_____

_____

Using the Strategy

Using your notes from one of the topics above, write a paragraph or two describing or narrating the topic.

_____

_____

_____

_____

_____

_____

_____

_____

Evaluating the Writer's Use of the Strategy

Form a small group with several other writers and read the paragraphs you wrote for the preceding question. Have your readers fill out the evaluation report included here.

Evaluation Report

1. Names of the readers: _____

2. Summarize the main point of the paragraph. _____

   _____

3. What details help the writer achieve his or her purpose? _____

   _____

   _____

4. Could other, better details have been included? _____

_____

_____

_____

5. What suggestions for revision can you offer? _____

_____

_____

_____

6. What is the most effective aspect of this paragraph? _____

_____

_____

ILLUSTRATION

Recognizing the Strategy

In the two selections below, both writers are using the strategy of illustration. You can see this more clearly by examining the structure of each paragraph. Write the thesis for each paragraph and list the examples that support it.

> One by one the American landmarks disappear. They are the victims of neglect, of ignorance, and the profit motive.
> On Cranberry Street in Brooklyn Walt Whitman's place was boarded up, waiting for the demolition crew. The city planned in its place one of those huge rabbit-warren housing projects that are the despair of urban sociologists and the delight of a few favored big-time real estate operators.
> Are there any who care today about the place where Whitman set his own type for the first edition of *Leaves of Grass?*
> New Yorkers also dismantled Mark Twain's house in the Village area and the Pennsylvania Station, one of the great architectural masterpieces of modern Western building.

A dozen other cultural and historical landmarks have gone the way of all American progress. The Gettysburg battlefield (not the cemetery) may become part of a building development although Gettysburg itself is now so desecrated by neon lights and shill booths it probably won't make much difference. (Harry Golden, "A Farewell to Landmarks," *Long Live Columbus*)

Thesis: _____

_____

List of examples: _____

_____

_____

Like most shoes, running shoes are made with an outsole, midsole, and upper. But running shoes employ a few features that are not standard equipment on a pair of sneakers. The midsole, responsible for shock absorption on most running shoes, is the designers' favorite playground. One manufacturer hollowed out chambers of foam and filled them with an inert gas. Others have tried air pockets that inflate through a valve at the side of the shoe, canals cut out of the heel region that give on impact, or tiny holes beneath the ball of the foot that increase flexibility.

A new development in outsole design is the incorporation of removable plugs of hard rubber beneath the heel, ball of the foot, and other areas that get the most wear. When they are worn down, a runner simply pops in new ones. (Eric Perlman, "The Soul of a Running Shoe," *Science 82*)

Thesis: _____

_____

List of examples: _____

_____

_____

© 1984 Houghton Mifflin Company

Practicing the Strategy

Select two of the topics below and list three or four examples or points you could use in writing a paragraph that employs the strategy of illustration.

1. Food additives are found in many different types of manufactured food.

     a. _____

     b. _____

     c. _____

     d. _____

2. Among the films released in the last year or so, there were some excellent ones that were big money makers at the box office.

     a. _____

     b. _____

     c. _____

     d. _____

3. When it came to selecting phones for their homes, the only option most people had ten years ago, was to choose either a dial or a pushbutton phone. Now, there are a wealth of new options and conveniences on the phones people are buying.

     a. _____

     b. _____

     c. _____

     d. _____

4. Most low-calorie diets are similar in that they restrict or eliminate the same kinds of foods.

     a. _____

     b. _____

c. _____

d. _____

5. Professional football teams make large amounts of money from commercial products that carry the team name and colors. The variety of these products is amazing.

a. _____

b. _____

c. _____

d. _____

Using the Strategy

Using your notes for one of the topics above, write a paragraph developed by illustration.

_____

_____

_____

_____

_____

Evaluating the Writer's Use of the Strategy

Form a small group with several other writers and read the paragraphs that you wrote for the preceding question. Then have your readers fill out the following evaluation report.

Evaluation Report

1. Names of readers: _____

2. What is the thesis of the paragraph? _____

_____

3. Are the examples that illustrate the thesis well chosen? Why? _____

_____

_____

4. Could the writer have included other or better examples? _____

_____

_____

5. What suggestions for revision can you offer? _____

_____

_____

6. What is the most effective aspect of this paragraph? _____

_____

_____

COMPARISON/CONTRAST

Recognizing the Strategy

In the two selections below, the writers are using the strategy of comparison. Outline the structure of each selection in the space provided.

> The South is the land of the sustained sibilant. Everywhere, for the appreciative visitor, the letter "s" insinuates itself in the scene: in the sound of the sea and sand, in the singing shell, in the heat of the sun and sky, in the sultriness of the gentle hours, in the siesta, in the stir of birds and insects. In contrast to the softness of its music, the South is also cruel and hard and prickly. A little striped lizard, flattened along the sharp green bayonet of a yucca, wears in its tiny face and watchful eye the pure look of

death and violence. And all over the place, hidden at the bottom of their small sandy craters, the ant lions lie in wait for the ant that will stumble into their trap. (E. B. White, "The Ring of Time," *Essays of E. B. White*)

Thesis: _____

Point A: _____

Examples: _____

_____

Point B: _____

Examples: _____

_____

J. Anthony Lukas is a world-class pinball player who, between tilts, does some free-lance writing. In our city, he is No. ½. That is to say, he is one of two players who share pinball preeminence—two players whose special skills within the sport are so multiple and varied that they defy comparative analysis. The other star is Tom Buckley, of the *Times*. Pinball people tend to gravitate toward Lukas or Buckley. Lukas is a Lukasite. He respects Buckley, but he sees himself as the whole figure, the number "1". . . .

When [Lukas] was the *Times'* man in the Congo, in the early sixties, the post was considered a position of hardship, so he was periodically sent to Paris for rest and rehabilitation, which he got playing pinball in a Left Bank brasserie. He had perfected his style as an undergraduate at Harvard, sharing a machine at the *Crimson* with David Halberstam. . . . Lukas's father was a Manhattan attorney. Lukas's mother died when he was eight. He grew up, for the most part, in a New England community—Putney, Vermont—where he went to pre-prep and prep school. . . .

Buckley, slightly older than Lukas, has a spectacled and professorial look. He wears a double-breasted blazer, a buff turtleneck. He lives on York Avenue now. He came out of Beechhurst, Queens, and learned his pinball in the Army—in Wrightstown, New Jersey, in Kansas City, and he moved up through the pinball ranks from beginner to virtuoso on a machine in a Katz drugstore.

It is Buckley's manner to lean into the machine from three feet out. His whole body, steeply inclined, tics as he reinforces. . . . Lukas's address is like a fencer's *en garde*. He stands close to the machine, with one foot projecting under it. . . . (John McPhee, "The Pinball Philosophy," *Giving Good Weight*)

Thesis: _____

A/B: _____

_____

A/B: _____

_____

A/B: _____

_____

Practicing the Strategy

Select one of the sets of topics below. Then, in the space provided, list some points you might include in writing several paragraphs that explain how the two are similar or dissimilar.

1. pizza and tacos
2. Spanish and FORTRAN
3. Labor Day and July 4th
4. trains and planes
5. golf shoes and basketball shoes
6. fraternities/sororities and dorms
7. an old classic movie (such as *Gone with the Wind* or *Casablanca*) and a recent major movie
8. science fiction and fairy tales
9. rock groups and a string orchestra
10. history and political science
11. small towns and suburbs
12. owning your own farm and managing someone else's farm
13. the Superbowl and the Rose Bowl
14. a canoe and a rowboat

              Topic A   Topic B

_____   _____

_____   _____

———————————   ———————————

———————————   ———————————

———————————   ———————————

———————————   ———————————

Using the Strategy

Using your notes for either Topic A or Topic B, formulate a topic sentence and write a comparison paper at least several paragraphs in length.

——————————————————————————

——————————————————————————

——————————————————————————

——————————————————————————

——————————————————————————

——————————————————————————

——————————————————————————

——————————————————————————

——————————————————————————

Evaluating the Writer's Use of the Strategy

Form a small group with several other writers and read the papers that you have written for the preceding question. Then have your readers fill out this evaluation report.

Evaluation Report

1. Names of readers: _____

2. What is the thesis of the paper? _____

   _____

3. Does the thesis clearly state what the comparison is meant to show?

   _____ Explain _____

   _____

   _____

4. Are the points of comparison explained sufficiently? _____ If not,

   what needs more explanation? _____

   _____

   _____

5. What other points of comparison might the writer have used? _____

   _____

   _____

   _____

6. What suggestions for revision can you offer? _____

   _____

   _____

7. What is the most effective aspect of the paper? _____

   _____

   _____

CLASSIFICATION

Recognizing the Strategy

In the two selections below, the writers are using the strategy of classification. Outline the structure of each selection in the space provided.

It was once the common belief that the climate was determined by a large number of gods, each in charge of a specific variety of weather. Then came the major religions, and most people came to hold a more subdued point of view that suggested but a single god who got around a lot. Many still take this position, although the majority now ascribe to a theory of weather based largely on cloud formation, air pressure, wind velocity, and other aspects of science. Lastly, there are those who feel that the weather and what it does are entirely the province of honey-throated television announcers with big Magic Markers. So, then, we are presented with three basic theories as regards the controlling factor of weather:

A. God
B. Nature
C. Tone of Voice

To the casual observer it would appear that these three theories are widely disparate. That, of course, is the problem with casual observers. Their very casualness—that trait we once all found so attractive . . . so appealing . . . so devil-may-care—is precisely what makes them so quick to judge and therefore so frequently inaccurate. The more vigilant observer would unquestioningly be able to detect a rather striking similarity. That similarity being that all three theories are based quite simply on mere whim—God can change his mind, Nature can change her course, and Voice, as we all know only too well, can change its tone. (Fran Lebowitz, "Good Weather and Its Propensity to Frequent the Better Neighborhoods," *Metropolitan Life*)

Thesis: _____

_____

Groups of information: _____

_____

_____

When setting up a new aquarium, one of the primary concerns of the aquarist is that of balance. A balanced tank is essential to the success of a new aquarium. Balance in oxygen content, waste removal, and plant life is important, of course, but the choice of the main occupants of the tank, the fish, is perhaps the most important.

Three types of fish can be used to achieve a balanced aquarium, the first of which is the community type. Community fish are, as their name implies, non-aggressive. Many fish in this group are vegetarians and can be trusted not to eat other fish in the tank; but, even those fish that are carnivorous will be compatible with their brothers if they are properly fed. Mollies, Swordtails, and Angelfish are examples of community fish that can be safely kept in one tank.

The second type that will meet the requirement of balance is the rough-fish type. It is true that rough fish tend to be territorial (that is, they mark off an area in the tank that is "theirs"), and they will tolerate no intruders. These fish are aggressive to the point of killing any fish unable to defend itself. It would appear, then, that community fish are not compatible with this type of fish as they will be swiftly eaten. However, rough fish can be kept in the tank if two or three of approximately equal strength are selected and supplied with a separate flower pot, or other shelter, so each may claim his own territory. In this way the rough fish are prevented from fighting with each other and balance can be maintained in the tank. Firemouths, Convicts, and Silver dollars are members of the rough-fish type that can be kept in one tank, if they are provided with separate territories.

The third type, and perhaps the most essential to a balanced tank, is the scavenger type. Scavengers are a "universal" fish in that they are non-aggressive enough to be kept with community fish, and yet independent enough to be kept with rough fish. The scavenger's ability to live with all types of fish is important because he is the housekeeper of the aquarium. While the scavenger does not eat waste material, he does consume food that has accumulated at the bottom of the tank, which other fish won't eat. This eating habit is essential to the balanced tank because it prevents excess food from fouling the water. The Corydoras, the Algae-eater, and the Banjo catfish are all excellent scavengers and compatible in any tank.

A thorough knowledge of the three fish types and the fish that make up each type will save the novice aquarist many headaches later on. By carefully selecting compatible fish, the aquarist will achieve balance in his aquarium and assure himself of a successful tank. (James Weston, student writer)

Thesis: _____

_____

Groups of information: _____

_____

_____

Practicing the Strategy

Select two of the following topics and list three or four groups into which information about those topics could be organized.

1. kinds of colleges and universities
2. winter sports
3. types of recording devices
4. pesticides
5. popular music groups
6. energy sources
7. regional dialects
8. types of teachers
9. types of cars
10. types of gifts

Topic A	Topic B
_____	_____
_____	_____
_____	_____
_____	_____
_____	_____
_____	_____
_____	_____
_____	_____
_____	_____

Using the Strategy

Using your notes for one of the topics above, formulate a thesis and write a classification paper of at least several paragraphs.

_____

_____

_____

_____

_____

_____

_____

_____

_____

Evaluating the Writer's Use of the Strategy

Form a small group with several other writers and read the papers that you wrote for the preceding question. Then have your readers fill out this evaluation report.

Evaluation Report

1. Names of readers: _____

2. Has the writer formulated appropriate or useful groups? _____

   What more could be added to any of the groups? _____

   _____

   _____

3. What major groups are missing? _____

_____

4. Are the distinctions between the groups clear? _____ If not, which

   are the least clear? _____

_____

5. What suggestions for revision can you offer? _____

_____

_____

6. What is the most effective aspect of this paper? _____

_____

_____

PROCESS ANALYSIS

Recognizing the Strategy

In the two selections below, the writers are using the process strategy. Outline the structure of each selection in the space provided.

> Perhaps you'll be surprised to learn that all the much vaunted "intelligence" of computers consists of is the ability to count up to one. Yes, that's right. The ability to count from zero to one. All the logical and arithmetic circuits of a computer do is detect the absence or presence of an electronic impulse, defined as "zero" in the first case and "one" in the second. These impulses can be moved by transmitting them through wires, or the equivalent of wires, and stored either temporarily or permanently by using the impulses to trip switches which can be checked later to see if they remain in an on (one) or off (zero) condition. These banks of switches are called "memory" and can recreate the stream of impulses originally sent when called upon to do so. We speak of this process as "reading" memory.
>
> The trick is that patterns of impulses are assigned universal meanings by

us humans, and we are able to design other circuits which *interpret* these patterns into human-sensible language (numbers, letters, and punctuation) and are able to display them in that form on documents or on the face of a TV-like screen. (Donald R. Shaw, *Your Small Business Computer*)

Thesis: _____

Sequence of operations or actions: _____

_____

_____

By the time a dozen students came to him with painful skin rashes or ear infections, James McCutchan, University of North Carolina's student health service physician, was suspicious. And when they all told him they'd recently celebrated a Tar Heel basketball victory with a dip in a rented giant redwood hot tub, he notified the local health department, who in turn notified the federal Centers for Disease Control.

The students, say the health officials, may represent the worst known outbreak of infections from a hot tub–loving bacterium that began showing up in the late 1970s as the tubs and whirlpool baths became fashionable. Though all recovered, six of the students were treated with antibiotics, and one was hospitalized. . . .

Called *Pseudomonas aeruginosa*, the bacterium lives in soil, human skin and intestines, and in standing water. It thrives at warm temperatures, multiplying every 30 minutes. Hospitals have struggled for decades to control it in their therapeutic tubs.

The wooden hot tub is a particularly inviting habitat for the organism. It hides in the porous wood, reemerging even after cleaning to contaminate fresh water. ("Hot Tub-itis," *Science 83*)

Thesis: _____

_____

Sequence of operations or actions: _____

_____

_____

Practicing the Strategy

Select two of the topics listed below and outline the sequence for each process. Include some details to suggest how the steps will be explained.

1. how to milk a cow
2. how to go from the room you are now in to a nearby well-known landmark
3. how to register in your college or university
4. how to eat an oyster
5. how to play a popular video-arcade game
6. how a fuel-injected engine works
7. how to develop film
8. how to measure blood pressure
9. how to apply for a job
10. how to join the fraternity or sorority of your choice
11. how to build a campfire
12. how to play a favorite children's game

Topic A   Topic B

Sequence: _____   Sequence: _____

_____   _____

_____   _____

_____   _____

_____   _____

Using the Strategy

Using your notes from one of the topics above, formulate a thesis and write a process paragraph.

_____

_____

_____

_____

_____

_____

_____

_____

_____

_____

Evaluating the Writer's Use of the Strategy

Form a small group with several other writers and read the paragraphs that you wrote for the preceding question. Then have your readers fill out the evaluation report included here.

Evaluation Report

1. Names of readers: _____

2. What process is being explained? _____

3. Is there enough detail in each of the steps or sequences of action?

   _____ If not, what else could or should be included? _____

   _____

   _____

4. Is unnecessary information included? _____ If so, what? _____

   _____

   _____

5. Are the steps in the appropriate order? _____ If not, how might

   the material be reordered? _____

_____

_____

6. What suggestions for revision can you offer? _____

_____

_____

7. What is the most effective aspect of the paper? _____

_____

_____

CAUSAL ANALYSIS

Recognizing the Strategy

In the two selections below, the writers are using the strategy of causal analysis. Identify the cause-and-effect relationship in each selection in the space provided. Be sure to include all causes and effects.

> There have been a great many forces that have helped to shape the American household and the buildings that have kept it dry and warm and in some cases embellished it. The process of our domestication (some people might call it our becoming civilized, others our being tamed) has in some respects been slowed and in others hastened by our inability to stay put either physically or socially. Our mobility has revealed itself in our tastes in architecture, in our manners in the living room, and in the uses and characters of our parlors and dining rooms and kitchens. So, of course, has the wastefulness in which a nation overly rich in natural resources can indulge. So, too, has the inventiveness that has made our houses into museums of gadgets which replace servants that we have been, at least theoretically, rather embarrassed as good democrats to employ. Our beliefs in equality and our flouting of them have shaped our houses as surely as have our plentiful forests, our fascination with technology, and the surges of immigration of inexpensive labor from countries less fortunate than our own.
> (Russell Lynes, *The Domesticated Americans*)

_____

_____

_____

   The nightmare of the plague was compounded for the fourteenth century by the awful mystery of its cause. The idea of disease carried by insect bite was undreamed of. Fleas and rats, which were in fact the carriers, are not mentioned in the plague writings. Contagion could be observed but not explained and thus seemed doubly sinister. The medical faculty of the University of Paris favored a theory of poisonous air spread by a conjunction of the planets, but the general and fundamental belief, made official by a papal bull, was that the pestilence was divine punishment for man's sins. Such horror could only be caused by the wrath of God. "In the year of our Lord, 1348," sadly wrote a professor of law at the University of Pisa, "the hostility of God was greater than the hostility of men." (Barbara Tuchman, "History as Mirror")

_____

_____

_____

Practicing the Strategy

Choose two of the following situations and list all the possible causes you can think of *and* all the possible effects:

a. spending your junior year abroad
b. buying a personal computer
c. investing in the stock market
d. buying American-made products (not foreign)
e. living in the country (not city)

Situation	Causes	Effects
1. _____	_____	_____
	_____	_____
	_____	_____

	Situation	Causes	Effects
2.	_____	_____	_____
		_____	_____
		_____	_____

Using the Strategy

Using your notes for one of the situations above, write a cause-and-effect paragraph.

_____

_____

_____

_____

_____

Evaluating the Writer's Use of the Strategy

Form a small group with several other writers and read the paragraphs that you wrote for the preceding question. Then have your readers fill out this evaluation report.

Evaluation Report

1. Names of readers: _____

2. Cause-and-effect situation: _____
3. Are the cause-and-effect relationships in the paragraph plausible?

    _____ If not, why not? _____

   _____

Can you think of other effects the writer should consider? Name some.

_____

_____

4. What other suggestions for revision can you offer? _____

_____

_____

5. What is the most effective aspect of this cause-and-effect paragraph?

_____

_____

DEFINITION

Recognizing the Strategy

In the two selections below, the writers are using the definition strategy. Summarize each definition in the space provided.

> Known as the "Champagne of Italy," Asti Spumante is a sparkling white wine produced in the provinces of Asti, Alessandria and Cuneo in northern Italy's Piedmont region, which is better known for its great red wines. Asti Spumante is vinified mostly from the Moscato grape and is somewhat sweeter than true Champagne from France. It exudes a heady aroma and luscious soft taste that makes a superb accompaniment to a dessert of ripe pears or peaches. Although it is often served as an apéritif in the same way that Champagne is served, this is a mistake; it is best after a meal. A very small quantity of Asti Spumante is made by the traditional French process, the *méthode champenoise*, involving fermentation in bottles, but most of it is produced by the bulk, or *charmat* process, involving vinification under pressure in large vats and then bottling under pressure to retain the bubbles. Asti Spumante must attain a minimum alcohol level of 12 percent. Sometimes this wine can be found with *brut* added to its name, indicating that it has been vinified completely dry, but it still retains the taste of the Moscato grape. (Terry Robards, *The New York Times Book of Wine*)

Term defined: _____

Summary of the definition: _____

_____

_____

      I first heard the word "mellow" when I was a freshman in high school. I wasn't sure what my older brother, Jeff, meant when he said a friend of his had mellowed out as he grew older. My understanding of this word formed slowly, but now I use the word to mean a kind of calmness. A person who is mellow doesn't get angry quickly, and he can make a decision slowly and thoughtfully, not rashly. Mellow people seem to sit back and watch what is happening. They never seem hurried, harassed, or overbearing. Mellow people are like a sedative, calming down others around them.

      The word "mellow" can also be defined by its sound. Even if I had no idea of what the word means or how it applies to people, the easy sound of the word would make me think of something relaxed or quiet. A mellow sound is one that seems to float through the air as if it had wings. It cascades through your mind and leaves you with pleasant thoughts. Mellow is the kiss of the summer breeze as it plays around your face. Mellow is mild and amiable, a gentle combination of softness and serenity. (Student writer)

Term defined: _____

Summary of the definition: _____

_____

_____

Practicing the Strategy

Select two of the terms listed below and note some points to be included in a definition.

1. shibboleth
2. friend
3. boredom
4. logarithm
5. status
6. software

7. turncoat
8. snob
9. black hole in space
10. economic depression
11. religion
12. charisma

Term A: _____   Term B: _____

_____   _____

_____   _____

_____   _____

_____   _____

Using the Strategy

Using your notes for one of the terms above, write a definition paragraph.

_____

_____

_____

_____

_____

Evaluating the Writer's Use of the Strategy

Form a small group with several other writers and read the paragraphs that you wrote for the preceding question. Then have your readers fill out this evaluation report.

Evaluation Report

1. Names of readers: _____

2. Term defined: _____

3. For what audience is the definition written? _____

   What part of the definition is appropriate for that audience? _____

   _____

   What part of the definition is inappropriate? _____

   _____

4. Has the writer written a short or a stipulative definition? _____

5. What part of the definition needs clarification or more detail? _____

   _____ What is needed? _____

   _____

6. What other suggestions for revision can you offer? _____

   _____

   _____

7. What is the most effective aspect of this definition? _____

   _____

   _____

MORE PRACTICE IN USING THE STRATEGIES

Exercise 1

For the following subjects or topics, write two different thesis sentences and indicate in parentheses the strategy to be used in developing each topic.

Topic	Thesis 1	Thesis 2
Example: my college	My college has excellent recreational sports facilities. (illustration)	My college offers excellent preparation for law school. (argumentation)

solar energy

1. _____

_____

2. _____

_____

National Football League

1. _____

_____

2. _____

_____

Christmas

1. _____

_____

2. _____

_____

my state senator

1. _____

_____

2. _____

_____

beer and wine

1. _____

_____

2. _____

_____

vacation   1. _____

_____

2. _____

_____

Exercise 2

In the first part of this exercise you can practice recognizing definitions and in the second part you can practice writing definitions.

Provide an English word that has the same meaning as the word being defined. (More than one answer may be correct.)

Equivalent English
word

1. snuforpist: one who holds on tenaciously
   to an opinion or point of view   _____

2. a kneeple: a short, high-pitched, convul-
   sive sound uttered when nervous or
   amused   _____

3. to flurf: to expel gas noisily from the
   stomach through the mouth   _____

4. gorksmim: slow to comprehend, dull or
   obtuse, showing a lack of sense or intel-
   ligence   _____

5. brooble: a male athlete who is well
   known for his athletic ability   _____

Now it is your turn. Make up a word and write a definition for it that could fit an English word. Give your list to another writer or small group of writers and have them write an equivalent English word in the space provided.

Your word and definition   Equivalent English word

1. _____: _____

   _____

   _____   _____

2. _____: _____

   _____

   _____   _____

3. _____: _____

   _____

   _____   _____

4. _____: _____

   _____

   _____   _____

5. _____: _____

   _____

   _____   _____

Exercise 3

In the first six items below, a common task is described. On the line to the right indicate what pattern of development will be needed to complete the task. In the last six items a strategy of development is listed at the right. In the lines to the left fill in a common task requiring that strategy.

Task   Strategy needed

a. Trying to decide which of two different
   compact cars to buy   _____

b. Learning how to become a skilled chef who can cook a magnificent omelet   _____

c. Responding to a friend who asks what you meant when you said, "She's out to lunch—permanently."   _____

d. Telling someone how badly your favorite sports team played in the last game   _____

e. Explaining to a friend how your new redial phone works   _____

f. Filling out an auto accident report that asks for the sequence of events   _____

g. _____   classification

_____

_____

h. _____   definition

_____

_____

i. _____   illustration

_____

_____

j. _____   process

_____

_____

k. _____   comparison

_____

_____

l. _____   narration/description

_____

_____

Exercise 4

List three words and their definitions that were used among your family or in your neighborhood and that had a special meaning for you. When you have written your definitions, form a small group with several other writers and ask if they are familar with the word and definition that you've written.

<table>
<tr><td>Term</td><td>Definition</td></tr>
</table>

a. _____   _____

                                               _____

b. _____   _____

                                               _____

c. _____   _____

                                               _____

Exercise 5

Each of these opening sentences indicates the strategy of development that is to be used. Name the strategy and finish the paragraph.

a. Shopping from a catalog is better (or worse) than buying things in a store.

    Strategy: _____

    Your paragraph: _____

    _____

    _____

    _____

b. Where I grew up, being rich meant . . .

    Strategy: _____

Your paragraph: _____

_____

_____

_____

c. The only way I know of to get a refund from a large store is . . .

Strategy: _____

Your paragraph: _____

_____

_____

_____

d. The popular definition of Murphy's law is that if something can go wrong, it will. I often feel as if Murphy's law is operating whenever I am in a particular hurry to get somewhere.

Strategy: _____

Your paragraph: _____

_____

_____

_____

6
Paragraphs

TOPICAL PARAGRAPHS

Recognizing the Four Elements

Unity

To practice recognizing ideas that focus on a topic, ask yourself which of the following sentences might belong in a unified paragraph on each of the two topics listed below. Check the appropriate space at the right for each sentence.

	Yes	No

Topic: the popularity of personal computers

a. Many popular video-arcade games are now available for personal computers.

b. In most computers, information is stored magnetically on floppy disks.

c. Numerous components of personal computers manufactured in America are imported from Japan.

d. There are programs for personal computers that offer help with taxes, checking accounts, medical records, and bills to be paid.

e. Most personal computers are small enough to be easily portable, and some even come in a single unit that can be packed up like a suitcase.

Yes   No

Topic: shyness as a possible hereditary trait

a. Researchers have studied shyness in both identical and
fraternal twins.   ____   ____
b. Some people find it difficult to attend a social gathering
when they don't know many of the people.   ____   ____
c. Small children often become fearful when picked up by
strangers.   ____   ____
d. Jim and Ted, four-year-old identical twins, were ob-
served to be equally reluctant to enter a room before
their mother did.   ____   ____
e. Results of recent studies indicate that genes may have
more to do with shyness than with other aspects of
personality, such as conformity or confidence.   ____   ____

Completeness

Deciding whether or not a paragraph is complete depends on how much
the reader needs to know. To gain practice in making such decisions, read
the following sentences and indicate which reader (or readers) would need
to know the content of the sentence by placing the appropriate letters
(A, B, or C) on the line at the end of each sentence.

Topic: snow-making machines for ski resort areas
Possible readers: (A) skiers; (B) potential buyers of snow machines; (C)
environmentalists

a. Snow-making coverage on eight of our newer lifts (including the
Gondola) assures skiing for all abilities from Thanksgiving
through April.   ____
b. Snow guns, developed over three decades ago, produce a dense
snow that is similar to packed natural snow.   ____
c. Because machine-made snow is denser, it evaporates less and
leaves more water for spring run-off.   ____
d. Snow guns that use compressed air to convert water to snow
cost more to operate but make better snow at higher altitudes.   ____
e. The extra water added to mountain sides by means of snow
guns has killed off some plants because of high soil moisture.   ____

Listed below are three topics. You can practice working toward paragraph completeness by deciding what readers might need to know about

these topics. If you can, work with several other writers and list some items to include in a paragraph on each topic. If members of your group disagree about a possible entry on the list, try to work out an agreement based on what you know about paragraph completeness. You will need to decide who the readers of this paragraph would be.

Topic: college marching bands

_____

_____

_____

_____

Topic: nutritious versus convenient breakfast foods

_____

_____

_____

_____

Topic: possible danger to children in celebrating Halloween

_____

_____

_____

_____

Order

Using what you have learned in your text, identify the ordering sequence (general to particular, particular to general, whole to parts, question to answer, or effect to cause) in each of the following paragraphs. Explain in a sentence or two why you think the paragraph uses that order.

The essay from which this paragraph is taken argues that boards of directors in large companies are essentially useless.

> Board meetings are conducted with the splendor of a coronation and will introduce the outside directors to a style of living to which they are by no means accustomed, even from their years of public service. The meeting site is usually some lavish corporate headquarters, a mansion-conference center, an exclusive club, or a private room in a posh hotel or restaurant. Often it is some faraway vacation spot: board meetings during winter months have a habit of being scheduled in Caribbean conference centers. Transportation to and from gatherings is strictly first-class, including chauffeured limousines where the necessity of surface travel prevents the use of private jet or helicopter. Rare wines and rare meat make the dullest agenda palatable. (Timothy F. Bannon, "The Board Game," *Harper's*)

The order of this paragraph is _____

_____

_____

_____

This excerpt is from an article on the Welsh people and their ability to maintain a sense of their nationhood.

> Yet despite centuries of subjugation by the English, Wales has somehow managed to retain its own identity—recognizably a different nation, honoring different values, cherishing different styles, even possessing a different language, from its overwhelming English neighbor. It is a classic example—perhaps the classic example—of a small country defying all the odds of history, geography, economics, sociology and cultural pressure to retain a sense of its self. Fewer than three million people live in Wales, only a small minority of them actively working for Welshness, only a fifth of them speaking Welsh. Some 46 million people live in England, immediately next door, and massed behind them, armed with all the insidious weapons of modern communications and publicity, are countless more members of the rich, powerful and materialist Western world—all of them a constant threat, though they may not know it, to the fragile Welsh dimension. (Jan Morris, "The Unconquerable Welsh," *The New York Times Magazine*)

The order of this paragraph is _____

_____

_____

_____

The excerpt here is part of a discussion of government regulations for automobile safety.

Should the government require that new cars be equipped with airbags —cushions that inflate on impact to protect passengers in a crash? Like nuclear power, this is an issue where reasonable minds may differ, but reasonable minds are hard to find. To Ralph Nader, airbags have provided a litmus test of political virtue ever since the last Corvair rolled off the assembly line in the mid-Sixties. Nader bitterly denounced his protegee Joan Claybrook for not immediately requiring the devices when she was director of highway safety for Jimmy Carter. Opponents of airbags see them as the prime example of statist meddling. *Car and Driver*, a magazine for auto enthusiasts, refers to Nader and Claybrook as "Safety Nazis." (Robert M. Kaus, "Hot Airbags," *Harper's*)

The order of this paragraph is _____

_____

_____

_____

The following excerpt is from a biographical sketch of the author and politician Gore Vidal.

Since the beginning, Vidal has existed in exalted political company. Born Eugene Luther Gore Vidal in 1925, he spent most of the first 10 years of his life in Washington, with his maternal grandparents. His grandfather, Thomas Pryor Gore, was the first senator from the new state of Oklahoma. He was also blind from the age of 10. Vidal remembers those years in Washington as idyllic. He used to read to his grandfather from the Congressional Record and from the classics (the first book was *Tales from Livy* and, says Vidal, he's been a Romanophile ever since), and he used to accompany the senator to the Senate chamber and sit by him there. (Joshua Gilder, "Gore Vidal's Latest Escapade," *Saturday Review*)

The order of this paragraph is _____

_____

_____

_____

When several Nobel prize winners were asked about the future of psychology, they responded in various ways. Below are the first few paragraphs of each of their responses (from the December 1982 issue of *Psychology Today*) with the sentences listed out of order. Decide what the topics of the paragraphs are and then reorder the sentences within the paragraphs.

These sentences make up the first two paragraphs of a response by Isaac Bashevis Singer.

1. Because I believe in this, I think that psychology can never become a real science, let's say as physics or chemistry or even biology, because when you deal with free choice you can never know what free choice will do.
2. So psychology is limited as a science, but at the same time it is broader than other sciences because it deals with free choice.
3. In this respect, psychology and fiction are neighbors; more than neighbors, I would say—even relatives.
4. Although we are all products of causality, there is also some remnant of free choice left in us.
5. Psychology, like fiction, has huge limits, because psychology must not only investigate what human beings can do or did do, but also what they might have done.

Topic of paragraph 1: _____

_____

Order of sentences in paragraph 1: _____

Topic of paragraph 2: _____

_____

Order of sentences in paragraph 2: _____

These sentences are the first paragraph of a response by Rosalyn S. Yalow.

1. The probability of dying from cancer of the lung is very high if you smoke, but people aren't afraid of smoking.

2. The probability of a nuclear reactor accident is practically negligible, but there is all sorts of mass hysteria associated with it.
3. An interesting problem for psychology to investigate is what I call the almost phobic fear of radiation.
4. Why do people have almost phobic reactions, when scientific analysis says there is no real risk?
5. In their lack of enough knowledge of hard science they develop improper perceptions.
6. I think that social scientists have promoted these fears, by not knowing enough about radiation.

Order of the sentences: _____

These sentences comprise the first paragraph of a response by Arno Penzias.

1. I think we take for granted the amazingly subtle strengths that exist in the brain—not only in our brains but in the brains of dogs and chimpanzees and what-have-you.
2. And here we are trying to learn to make computers from the really crummy machines we have around us rather than from the wonderful machines we all have between our ears.
3. I don't know if I have anything to teach a psychologist, but psychologists have a tremendous amount to teach me.
4. Traditionally, science has learned from nature, just as Leonardo learned about airplanes by watching birds.
5. I think the big challenge to science in the next generation is to learn about how our own minds work, and those of other biological systems, and the guide should come from psychology.
6. They are so much more powerful and flexible than any machine we know how to build, think about building, or even hope to build.

Order of the sentences: _____

Listed below are the sentences of the first two paragraphs about the underground conditions of the earth in the Mammoth Lakes area in California. Decide what the topic of each paragraph is and then arrange the sentences in the order you find most effective.

1. But deep under this quiet California valley a whirlpool of molten rock snakes toward the surface.
2. Wherever you go, you see groups of hearty, pink-cheeked skiers heading for the hills.

3. Pine and fir dot the town's immaculate streets, which are lined with fancy resort hotels, quaint little restaurants, and condos.
4. In 1980 the scalding material had been six miles below the terrestrial floor; by 1981 it had risen three miles more.
5. Mammoth Lakes, California, lies within a ring of looming, snow-capped mountains that nuzzle the clouds.
6. They think they have come to the most peaceful spot on Earth.
7. And this past May dozens of geoscientists visiting the volatile region felt the rumble of magma surging upward yet again.

(Madeleine Lebwohl, "Magma Power," *Omni*)

Topic of paragraph 1: _____

Order of sentences in paragraph 1: _____

Topic of paragraph 2: _____

Order of sentences in paragraph 2: _____

Coherence

The paragraph below describes some of the problems encountered by a team of scientists climbing Mt. Everest for purposes of scientific research. As you read the paragraph, notice how the author maintains coherence. Identify and discuss some of these devices in the space provided at the end of the paragraph. Include both the words (or phrases) and the line numbers for ease of reference.

1. It was hard to call it science when physician Peter Hackett dangled
2. upside down on a sheer rock face 8,000 feet above his next stopping
3. place. And it was hard to call it science when medical researcher Chris
4. Pizzo misplaced his ice ax, grabbed a flimsy aluminum tent pole and
5. marched toward the summit of Everest in a glorious quest for data.
6. But science it was when the 1981 American Medical Research Expedi-
7. tion to Everest transformed the mountain into the highest research
8. laboratory on Earth. (From Eric Perlman, "For a Breath of Thin Air,"
    Science 83)

Coherence devices:

1. Pronouns: _____

_____

2. Repetitive structure: _____

_____

3. Contrast: _____

_____

4. Transitions between sentences: _____

_____

When paragraphs are tied together with transitions, the first sentence of the next paragraph often refers back to the previous paragraph to tie the two together. The sentences that follow are the opening sentences of the new paragraphs. What do you think the topic of the previous paragraph was? After you write your answer, compare it with someone else's, if possible, to see whether or not you and other readers agree.

1. Although science fiction did gain its popularity in the cheap pulp magazines, today, with millions of avid readers, sci-fi writers are inclined to take a loftier view of their enterprise.

   The topic of the previous paragraph was _____

   _____

2. While enacting business tax cuts is one example of probusiness environment, another is the rapid expansion of convention sites in the state.

   The topic of the previous paragraph was _____

   _____

3. Ironically, the same conditions that have enabled revolutionary movements to flourish in Latin America have also helped speed the expansion of evangelical sects.

   The topic of the previous paragraph was _____

   _____

4. Despite a lifetime of political activism in France, Harold Le Man has stayed away from politics since moving to the U.S.

   The topic of the previous paragraph was _____

   _____

5. Finally, after the lengthy week of jury selection was over, there was the trial, one of the most elaborately staged in modern history.

The topic of the previous paragraph was _____

_____

6. But the armed services are only part of the problem of resisting ideas whose time has come; the Defense Department has evolved into a grouping of large, rigid bureaucracies which embrace the past and adapt new technology to fit traditional methods and missions.

The topic of the previous paragraph was _____

_____

Drafting and Revising Paragraphs

Exercise 1

The sentences below contain a collection of data from recent research on sleep. Decide the topics of several paragraphs and the sentences that will be included in those paragraphs, and then write either two or three paragraphs. Add transitions where they are needed. Feel free to use only the data that you think necessary for the paragraphs.

1. There are three principal states of mind in humans: waking, sleeping, and dreaming.
2. If people stay up too long without sleep, their bodies generate neurochemicals that literally force them to go to sleep.
3. An electroencephalogram detects brain waves.
4. During the three principal states of mind, brain waves show distinct patterns of electrical activity.
5. Sleep-deprived animals generate neurochemicals in their cerebrospinal fluid.
6. Brain waves represent very small currents and voltages produced by the electrical circuitry of the brain.
7. The folk-medicine explanation of sleep is that it has a restorative effect, allowing the body to perform certain restorative activities not as easily performed during the day when people are awake.

8. Cerebrospinal fluid of sleep-deprived animals induces sleep when injected into other animals who are perfectly wide awake.
9. Typical strengths of brain-wave signals are measured in microvolts.
10. Evidence for the explanation that the body needs sleep for restoration is very sparse.
11. The electroencephalograph was invented by a German psychologist, Hans Berger.

Paragraph topic: _____

Sentences to be used in that paragraph: _____

Paragraph topic: _____

Sentences to be used in that paragraph: _____

Paragraph topic: _____

Sentences to be used in that paragraph: _____

Your paragraphs:

_____

_____

_____

_____

_____

_____

_____

_____

_____

_____

Exercise 2

The writer of the paper included here collected information on the autistic child and wrote the following draft. This draft, however, which is mainly a list of unorganized details, needs to be reordered. Suggest to the writer categories for organizing the material. She would appreciate any other suggestions you can offer for making this a more effective paper.

> Though there is much yet to be learned about autism in children, some information is available on the symptoms and behavior of the autistic child. The autistic child is extremely withdrawn and shows little interest in other people or in the normal activities of childhood. Sometimes if a child is autistic from birth, a mother has an uneasy feeling that her baby is unusual in some way, but is unable to put her finger on what is wrong. Some of the first signs and symptoms of autism can be detected as early as infancy but other autistic children may develop normally until about the age of two. While no autistic child is exactly like another, such children display many distinct characteristics. The most obvious characteristic is extreme isolation. Such children pay more attention to objects than to humans. Autistic children often develop a dependence on routines. When there is a change in their daily routines, they may become very emotional. Autistic children are also unable to develop the usual play activities. When they are young, their only occupation is to hold, feel, twist, and turn objects in their hands. As babies they will not show signs in responding to their mothers' presence as normal babies do. By the age of two they begin to exhibit behavior problems. (Student writer)

Categories for reordering the information: _____

_____

_____

_____

Other revision suggestions: _____

_____

_____

_____

Exercise 3

The drafts of these student paragraphs lack transitional words and phrases. In the space provided, rewrite each paragraph and add transitions where they are needed. Feel free to rearrange the sentences and to reorder the words in each sentence.

Cooperative education is the ultimate work/study program. More and more students are choosing to learn while they earn. A national study of co-op programs found that even five-year work/study programs are worth the extra time. Co-op students more than earn back the cost of an extra year's tuition, living expenses and wages because co-op students generally find employment more quickly after graduation and earn starting salaries five to ten per cent higher than people without previous work experience with a business firm. Students in engineering, business, and health-related fields, who comprise the greatest number of co-op students, have few problems finding jobs closely related to their field of study. (Student writer)

Your revised version: _____

_____

_____

_____

_____

_____

_____

It is universally known that the reason for a child to attend school is to receive an education. Music is an education too although in many schools it is not stressed. Music education should be a regular class in primary schools. A child has the choice of whether or not he will continue his music education. The child needs to be introduced to music throughout his primary schooling. A primary introduction to music is a must for a child to be able to make the choice of whether or not to continue his music education. (Student writer)

Your revised version: _____

_____

_____

_____

_____

_____

_____

Exercises 4 and 5 involve looking at all four requirements of paragraphs: unity, completeness, order, and coherence. If possible, complete these exercises as part of a small group working together to help each other learn to write more effective paragraphs.

Exercise 4 Offering Editorial and Revision Assistance

The two paragraphs here were written by college freshmen learning how to write better paragraphs. After you and your group read through these examples, offer your help both as an editor and as a rewriter. Comment on what is good about the paragraph and what ought to be rewritten; then follow your editorial suggestions as you rewrite the paragraphs.

> Television has a distinct advantage over the use of the radio and newspaper as a means for interpreting information. The radio is limited. It cannot use a visual picture or diagram in explaining the meaning of its program. A newspaper is bound also. A newspaper can use illustrations, but it lacks the convenience of the audio approach of the television. It takes time and a considerable amount of effort to sit down and read a newspaper.

Editorial comments: _____

_____

_____

_____

_____

_____

Rewritten version: _____

_____

_____

_____

_____

_____

_____

College has become a fad, a great idea, a big triumph. Everyone likes the dumping idea. It gets kids out of the parents' hair, helps fight crime in big cities, fights unemployment, and even provides an opportunity for every Congressman to reach the individual with a free grant to pay the college expenses of their constituents' children. Even the universities are supporting the idea of everyone going to college because it brings in more revenue and provides an excuse to ask for additional funds. The sad fact, however, is that sending the unmotivated and disinterested student to college doesn't do anything for the quality of education, and that is what college is supposed to be about. It's time to decide whether or not we care to support the biggest babysitting network in the world, or if higher education is going to mean learning. Some people just don't belong.

Editorial comment: _____

_____

_____

_____

Rewritten version: _____

_____

_____

_____

_____

_____

_____

Exercise 5 Finding Your Own Examples

1. Begin this project by finding a sample paragraph in a magazine or text-book and changing it so that one element (either unity, completeness, order, or coherence) is not adequately present.

2. Rewrite the paragraph here: _____

_____

_____

_____

_____

_____

3. Ask another group of writers to comment on the paragraph. Their job is to spot the weakness that you have introduced. Be sure that they indicate clearly whether the problem is one of unity, completeness, order, or coherence and that they offer some reason, proof, or example of what is causing the problem.

Comments from another writer or small group of writers:

_____

_____

_____

_____

_____

Peer Evaluation

Writers need assistance from other writers. This exercise in gathering feedback is designed to help you learn how readers react to your writing. As you fill out peer evaluation reports for other writers, you will also be sharpening critical abilities that you need for your own writing.

1. Write a paragraph on one of the following topics or on a topic of your own choosing. Number the sentences for ease of reference.
   a. your favorite form of exercise
   b. a sport you follow regularly
   c. your career choice
   d. the purpose of a group that you belong to
   e. your favorite type of movie
   f. your reaction to a style of clothing that was popular five or ten years ago

Your paragraph:

_____

_____

_____

_____

_____

_____

_____

2. Have several participants in a small group evaluation session read your
    paragraph. After they have discussed your paragraph, have them fill in
    this evaluation report as a group.

===

Evaluation Report

Names of readers: _____

Unity

What is the paragraph about? _____

_____

_____

Is there a topic sentence? If so, which one is it? _____

_____

_____

Does the paragraph focus on one idea? Which sentences are definitely and

clearly related to the main idea? _____

_____

_____

Which sentences are not clearly related to the topic? _____

_____

_____

Completeness

Describe the type of reader for whom you think this paragraph is

intended. _____

_____

_____

Does the paragraph provide as much information as the reader needs?

_____

_____

_____

What else might readers need to know? _____

_____

_____

What information, proof, or examples in the paragraph are unnecessary?

_____

_____

_____

Order

What is the ordering pattern of this paragraph? _____

_____

_____

Is every sentence in the appropriate order? _____

_____

If not, which sentence (or sentences) is (are) out of order? Where should

they be placed? _____

_____

Is there a clear direction of movement? _____ If so, describe it. _____

_____

Coherence

Is the paragraph generally coherent? _____

_____

Which pronouns help link the sentences together? _____

_____

Does repetition enhance coherence? _____ If so, where? _____

_____

Do contrasts help to tie the paragraph together? _____ Where?

_____

List the transition words used in the paragraph. _____

_____

Generally, what are the strong points of this paragraph? _____

_____

_____

What suggestions do you have for the writer to improve this paragraph?

_____

_____

_____

SPECIAL PARAGRAPHS

Introductory Paragraphs

Introductory paragraphs either suggest what you intend to do in the paper or are attention-getting devices that capture readers' interest and make them want to read what you have to say. Some introductory paragraphs do both.

Exercise 1

Read the following introductory paragraphs and evaluate their effectiveness. If possible, compare your evaluations with those of at least two other writers.

> In an anecdote popular among evolutionary biologists, J. B. S. Haldane is said to have met once with a group of British theologians. They asked him what he was able to learn about the creator from a study of his creation. "An inordinate fondness for beetles," the noted biologist reportedly replied. That story may come as no surprise to gardeners who encounter these insects in great abundance, but its real meaning lies not in the number of beetles, which is vast, but in the number of species of the Coleoptera, which is larger than that of any other animal order. Next to the beetles in species richness come the flies, or Diptera, and together these two groups have more recognized species than the entire remainder of the animal kingdom. This somewhat surprising information leads to the inquiry of why there should be so many species of small insects. Scientists seek an answer more empirically rooted than Haldane's whimsical reply to his ministerial associates. (Excerpt from Harold Morowitz, "Beetles, Ecologists, and Flies," *Science 82*)

I'd rate this introduction as _____

because _____

_____

> Maturity. It takes such a long time to reach that stage. But how does one know when he or she is really fully grown or developed? There are so many steps and stages that we have to go through to become mature, but how can we be sure that we've finally reached that supposedly utmost stage? (Student writer)

I'd rate this introduction as _____

because _____

_____

      From monarch to farmer, the Danes are balletomanes. But for more than two centuries they kept their special brand of classical and romantic ballet locked up within their ancient kingdom. It was not until the 1950s that the Royal Danish Ballet ventured forth to enchant London and other European capitals with its bounding dancers and its effervescent repertory. In short order, the company convinced international audiences that ballet at its best is not exclusively Russian, and that Danish ballet is also made of prime materials. (Excerpt from Walter Terry, "The Royal Danes Are Coming," *Saturday Review*)

I'd rate this introduction as _____

because _____

_____

Exercise 2

Listed below are three topics. Using methods described in the textbook or illustrated in the examples above, write at least two possible opening sentences for each of the topics.

1. Your solution for a common daily annoyance (alarm clocks that don't go off, pens that suddenly don't work in exams, etc.)

    Opening sentence 1: _____

    _____

    Opening sentence 2: _____

    _____

2. The advantages (or disadvantages) of buying health food products

    Opening sentence 1: _____

    _____

Opening sentence 2: _____

_____

3. The increase of crime in your town or city

Opening sentence 1: _____

_____

Opening sentence 2: _____

_____

Transitional Paragraphs

The examples and explanation in your text have shown several methods for signaling changes in content between one part of your paper and the next. Using these as guides, help a friend who has asked for your assistance in writing a transitional paragraph in a long essay on jogging. Having discussed the benefits of jogging, she now wants to explain how to jog. Offer her at least two examples for switching directions. Since transitional paragraphs can be quite short, your examples can also be brief.

Transition 1: _____

_____

_____

Transition 2: _____

_____

_____

Concluding Paragraphs

Concluding paragraphs either strengthen the message of the essay or are merely mechanical. How would you rate the following examples? Explain your answer, and if possible, compare your evaluations with those of several other readers.

I do not claim that my proposals will solve all of our defense problems, but these or similar major changes can set us on the right course. Congressional action is needed on these organizational issues—the most important defense problem facing our nation. Additional money is badly needed for defense, but without major realignment, we will neither achieve the necessary capability nor spend the money as wisely as we should. The critical question is whether we will show the wisdom to do as the British did, or whether we will muddle along as we have in the past until some crisis or disaster awakens us to the need for change. (Excerpt from David C. Jones, "What's Wrong with Our Defense Establishment," *The New York Times Magazine*)

Your evaluation: _____

_____

_____

Without the influence of television I feel that I would be a little bit different than I am now. I would probably not possess exactly the same opinions. Nor would I have the same likes and dislikes. Perhaps television influences me so strongly that I might even act differently. Thus taking into account all of this, I feel that television has and does play a significant role in my life. (Student writer)

Your evaluation: _____

_____

_____

Entertainment can take many different forms. There are live performances such as rock concerts, sporting events, or a ballet; group events such as a party or picnic; and individual activities such as reading or drawing. All of these, along with many others, can be entertainment for someone if the person enjoys the activity at the time he participates in it. (Student writer)

Your evaluation: _____

_____

_____

7

Sentences

EXPANDING AND COMBINING SENTENCES

Expanding by Modification

Exercise 1

Locate the subject word plus the verb and the object word in the predicates of the following sentences. Draw a circle around these words. Then find the adjectives, adverbs, phrases, and clauses that serve as modifiers in these sentences. Underline the modifiers.

1. The hospital, a simple, white building with a pervasive smell of disinfectant, gets its clients from the well-to-do upper northwestern section of Washington, D. C.
2. A prime example of the decline of basic industry in America is the troubled steel industry, presently operating its mills at about 35 percent capacity.
3. Slick, well-groomed national newscasters with their smooth delivery and self-assurance, strongly affect the way I think about important events reported on TV.
4. In 1982 John Hinckley was acquitted on grounds of insanity of shooting President Reagan, after a trial that consisted almost entirely of a clash of well-paid psychiatrists.
5. Isolated from the bustle of the big cities, my home town of Grandview is located on a quiet, two-mile-wide lake in a pine-scented valley.
6. Eugene Debs, the champion of the working man, ran unsuccessfully for president five times, once from a federal prison.
7. During the last forty years in which nuclear weapons have been in existence, nobody has been under any illusions about the horrifying consequences of using them.
8. Brent, my best friend, and I waited hesitantly in the huge, empty gym for the coach to notice us standing there.

9. Below the low-slung tree branches you could just barely see the last golden rays of sunshine that managed to pierce the darkness.
10. I have vivid memories of waking up that cold winter morning, the first day of vacation, and looking out the window at the mounds of white snow which had quietly accumulated during the night.

Exercise 2

In each of the three sentences that follow, add adjectives and adverbs either before or after the italicized words. Write two sentences with a different set of modifiers in each sentence.

1. The *child ate* his *dinner.*
   Example: The sullen *child* slowly *ate* his overcooked *dinner.*

   a. _____

   _____

   b. _____

   _____

2. *Salesmen demonstrate* their *products.*

   a. _____

   _____

   b. _____

   _____

3. *Sports fans follow* their team's *scores.*

   a. _____

   _____

   b. _____

   _____

Exercise 3

Using one of the versions you've written for each of the three sentences in Exercise 2, expand the sentence by including phrases or clauses that answer one or more of these questions:

How?
When?
Where?
Why?
In what manner?

Example: While watching TV, the sullen *child* slowly *ate* his overcooked *dinner* of meatloaf and peas, which lay shriveled on his plate.

1. _____

   _____

   _____

2. _____

   _____

   _____

3. _____

   _____

   _____

Exercise 4

When sentences are not modified by adjectives, adverbs, phrases, and clauses that give the reader more specific details, the reader lacks information about the writer's topic. This can leave a number of unanswered questions in readers' minds. How many questions can you ask about each of the sentences below, which lack adequate modification?

Example: One night, after a basketball game, I was driving home and had my first car accident.

Some questions about this sentence that might occur to the reader:

Was it late at night?
What were the weather conditions?
Was the basketball game a professional one or a local school game?
What kind of car was being driven?
How old was the car?
How experienced was the driver?
What happened to cause the accident?
How much damage resulted from the accident?
Was anyone hurt?
Was anyone else in the car?

1. In our high school we didn't have many activities to get involved with.
   Some questions that might occur to the **reader:**

   _____

   _____

   _____

   _____

   _____

   _____

2. My home has always been a special place to me.
   Some questions that might occur to the reader:

   _____

   _____

   _____

   _____

   _____

   _____

3. Growing up in a poor, rough neighborhood, he became more and more determined to find better things later on.
   Some questions that might occur to the reader:

   _____

   _____

   _____

   _____

   _____

   _____

   _____

Combining by Coordination

Exercise 1

In the sentences below, similar elements are joined into pairs or series. Identify these similar elements by underlining and then numbering each item in a group of coordinates, as shown in the following example:

To understand more about the physical conditions involved when people shoot guns and to gain insights into why some people are excellent marksmen, two researchers hooked up hundreds of shooters to machines that monitor brain wave patterns, heartbeat, the skin's electrical response, muscle tension, and respiration during a shooting session.

1. The type of attitude we display toward our friends, superiors, subordinates, and others around us may make the difference between getting a job or not and making a friend or an enemy, and it may even influence whether or not we have a good day.

2. College professors mainly lecture and organize the course, while their assistants answer questions, give and grade tests, and run help sessions.

3. If you are eating dinner with your family, you are probably not watching your manners as closely as you might if you were out with a date at an expensive restaurant or at an important business luncheon with your boss.

4. Recombined genes are little more than tools to improve yield volume, obtain purer yields, and improve the culture in which antibiotics are grown.

5. We are living in an information age in which the advent of microprocessors and space satellites are touching and changing every field of knowledge, almost all forms of commerce, and the foreign policies of all nations.

Exercise 2

Combine the similar elements given here into a sentence.

1. Mary lost ten pounds. She bought some new clothes. She cut off the scraggly ends of hair from an old permanent.

   Your combined sentence: _____

   _____

   _____

2. In order to build better computers, the company needed chemists to develop special polymers. They also needed physicists to study how light passes through optical fibers. They also needed psychologists to study how people interact with machines.

   Your combined sentence: _____

   _____

   _____

   _____

3. One of the more significant sports events in the world is the European Cup Finals in Soccer. The Rose Bowl is an equally well known competition. Another competition with audiences all over the world is the Wimbledon Tournament in England.

   Your combined sentence: _____

   _____

   _____

   _____

4. There are several methods for becoming a better speller. You ought to use the dictionary frequently to check words you don't know, and you should write the word in a notebook also. Say the word to yourself, and try to write it in a sentence too.

   Your combined sentence: _____

   _____

   _____

   _____

5. Cable TV is cutting into the national networks' market. Pay cable is also a strong competitor. Videodiscs and videotape recordings of movies are other competitors for the viewer's attention.

   Your combined sentence: _____

   _____

   _____

   _____

6. Jonas Salk, who developed the first polio vaccine, was born in New York in 1914. In 1934 he graduated from the College of the City of New York. He then earned his medical degree at the New York University College of Medicine five years later.

Your combined sentence: _____

_____

_____

_____

7. For athletic ability it is important that the body be able to deliver oxygen through a person's system. Also, lactic acid from exercise must be removed. Another requirement is a large respiratory volume and high systolic pressure to compensate for physical exertion.

Your combined sentence: _____

_____

_____

_____

Combining by Subordination

Exercise 1

In the following sentences, identify the subordinate elements by underlining them.

1. Because of the poor performance of his product, the manufacturer was unable to convince any of his customers that he deserved their confidence.
2. We have all played games, cards or Monopoly, with people who hate to lose, who will bend the rules or even cheat in order to win.
3. While Washington, Adams, and Madison all believed in the necessity of an educated citizenry, Jefferson and Franklin became better known advocates of the concept because they were more prolific writers on the subject.
4. With lower production costs, Canada's automotive industry is flourishing, particularly the Canadian-owned independent parts industry where production levels have increased over 500 percent in the period from 1965 to 1980.

5. Although many different approaches have been tried to curb drunk driving, approaches such as mandatory jail sentences, stiff fines, license suspension, and higher drinking-age laws, the number of accidents due to drunk driving continues to increase every year.

6. Asbestos-related disease, one of technology's unfortunate side effects, is a medical, social, and economic problem of far-reaching consequences that has been developing quietly for over thirty years.

7. The author Fran Lebowitz says that everyday life in Los Angeles can probably be best understood by realizing that most of its inhabitants would be happiest with a phone book that indicates the subscriber has four phone lines, sixteen extensions, and a fiercely guarded unlisted number.

8. Owing to weather delays, my plane from London reached New York at an hour when there was no further service to Chicago.

9. Electronics, already the tenth largest industry in the world, with present sales of over $20 billion, is projected to become the world's fourth largest industry by 1990.

10. While some video games confront the player with orderly rows of figures and patterns of action that can be memorized in order to succeed, other video games are more challenging because there are an infinite number of ways to succeed and fail.

Exercise 2

In each of the pairs of sentences below, reduce one sentence to a clause or phrase and include it as part of the other sentence.

1. Storytelling is an old art with a long heritage. Storytelling is enjoying a revival, with storytellers appearing in coffee houses, college auditoriums, theaters, libraries, schools, and so on.

_____

_____

_____

2. Clinton County used to be mainly an agricultural area. It has recently attracted more industry.

_____

_____

_____

3. The old woman sat in her rocking chair on the porch. She watched her grandchildren race by on their bikes.

_____

_____

_____

4. I forgot to set my alarm, and I woke up late for class. I missed the first ten minutes of the exam.

_____

_____

_____

5. The air in the city has been polluted by automobiles and industry. It is no longer fit to breathe.

_____

_____

_____

6. He was bored with the president's talk. He got up angrily and stamped out of the room.

_____

_____

_____

7. Americans are very concerned about their health and weight. Diet soda has steadily continued to gain in popularity.

_____

_____

_____

8. Astronomers now use radio telescopes to look for interstellar hydrogen. It is the most abundant material in the universe.

_____

_____

_____

9. The U. S. Metric Board was created to help Americans convert to the metric system. After six years, it fell prey to budget slashing and was discontinued.

_____

_____

_____

10. Jim was his major competition in the fifty-yard dash. Jim had already won two medals in other track events that day.

_____

_____

_____

Exercise 3

The paragraph below needs more subordination. Suggest where the author can combine clauses and phrases by subordination. You can either mark in the text or rewrite in the space provided below.

Television coverage can unduly influence the outcome of a presidential

election. This is true, for example, in debates. In debates, the candidates

are offering their views on national political issues, but many people judge

the candidates by their appearance and manner. A good example of this

was the Nixon-Kennedy debate. Mr. Nixon appeared sloppy and even unshaven. Mr. Kennedy appeared neat and well groomed. Mr. Kennedy talked with a lot of self-assurance and stood at ease on the platform. Mr. Nixon, however, was obviously nervous. He mopped his forehead with a handkerchief and wouldn't even look straight into the TV camera. Mr. Kennedy obviously pleased people with his appearance, but Mr. Nixon did not. (Student writer)

_____

_____

_____

_____

_____

_____

_____

_____

_____

_____

_____

_____

The Relation of Combination to Purpose

Exercise 1

Listed below are five base sentences, each with a list of clauses offering more information that could be used to expand the sentence. Write two expanded versions of each sentence for each purpose given. If possible, do the exercise with several other writers.

   The sentences included here were all taken from articles in popular magazines. You can compare your versions with the original sentences shown at the end of this chapter. What is the emphasis in the original sentences?

1. Base sentence: I. M. Pei does not normally design relatively modest hotels.
   Material for expansion:
   a. I. M. Pei is an architect
   b. he has created the following:
      the East Building of the National Gallery in Washington
      the New York City Convention and Exhibition Center
      some of the most conspicuous skyscrapers of the last decade
   c. a relatively modest hotel is the following
      one with 325 rooms
      a low-rise hotel

Purpose 1: Stress Mr. Pei's accomplishments. _____

_____

_____

_____

Purpose 2: Stress the fact that Mr. Pei is designing a hotel that is quite different from his normal designs. _____

_____

_____

_____

2. Base sentence: A storm recently ripped through California's Altamont Pass.
    Material for expansion:
    a. several hundred windmills have been installed in Altamont Pass
    b. the windmills capture energy from the wind
    c. winds whistle through Altamont Pass
    d. these winds are powerful

Purpose 1: Stress the strength of the winds blowing through Altamont Pass. _____

_____

_____

Purpose 2: Stress the fact that Altamont Pass is a place where wind is being harnessed for energy. _____

_____

_____

_____

3. Base sentence: A friend of mine argues that America is rife with snobbery and obsessed with status.
    Material for expansion:
    a. my friend argued this when writing in another magazine
    b. my friend offers evidence for his statement
    c. his evidence is that people will pay extra for a shirt with an alligator sewn on it
    d. the alligator on the shirt is little

Purpose 1: Stress the connection between the alligator on the shirt and

status. _____

_____

_____

_____

Purpose 2: Stress the fact that people will pay extra for status symbols. __

_____

_____

_____

4. Base sentence: When I first heard of it, I could hardly believe it.
   Material for expansion:
   a. garbage is collected twice a week in the city of Tucson
   b. garbage is collected in big, plastic bags
   c. some of these bags are opened
   d. the contents of these bags are painstakingly examined, classified, weighed, and recorded
   e. this work is done by students
   f. these students are from the University of Arizona

Purpose 1: Stress what is done with some garbage. _____

_____

_____

_____

Purpose 2: Stress the fact that garbage is being studied at the University of Arizona. _____

_____

_____

_____

5. Base sentence: A vestige of free enterprise in the Soviet Union is the private plot.
   Material for expansion:
   a. these plots are the chief vestige of free enterprise
   b. there are millions of these plots
   c. these plots provide perhaps one-quarter of the food consumed by the Soviet citizens
   d. there are 270 million Soviet citizens

Purpose 1: Stress the widespread practice of cultivating private plots in the Soviet Union. _____

_____

_____

_____

Purpose 2: Stress the identity of the main vestige of free enterprise in the Soviet Union. _____

_____

_____

_____

Exercise 2

The following facts appeared in a *Time* story on cocaine use (*Time*, April 11, 1983, pp. 22–31). Write two different paragraphs with expanded sentences. For each paragraph, answer one of the questions below.

Drug counselors estimate that among the 4 to 5 million Americans who use cocaine regularly, 5 percent to 20 percent (approximately 200,000 to 1 million people) are profoundly dependent on it.

New Federal antidrug task forces are being formed in dozens of cities.

It is estimated that about 45 tons of cocaine reach the market in a year.

Recently, the F.B.I. has been assigned to drug cases along with the Drug Enforcement Administration (DEA).

Cocaine is probably a $25 billion business.

A Yankelovich survey found that blue-collar workers are more likely than professionals to have tried cocaine.

11 percent of U.S. adults admit to having sampled cocaine.

There are 2,500 federal agents assigned to cut cocaine traffic.

Between 1979 and 1981, the number of coke-heads admitted to federally funded treatment programs rose by more than half, from 1,961 to 3,393.

A federal law allows the government to seize property bought with drug profits.

In a recent year, federal enforcement agencies seized drug profits of $100 million in cash, $40 million worth of aircraft, and $20 million in real estate.

In the last few years, the number of Americans who have used cocaine has risen from 15 million to 20 million.

1. How widespread is cocaine use? Write a paragraph with expanded sentences stressing the answer to this question.

_____

_____

_____

_____

_____

_____

_____

_____

_____

_____

2. What is being done by the government to curb the selling of cocaine?

_____

_____

_____

_____

_____

_____

_____

_____

_____

_____

_____

_____

Exercise 3

In the following excerpt from a student essay, the writer does not use subordination or coordination appropriately. Instead, she sometimes uses coordination when elements are unequal, and subordinates more important elements to less important elements. Help her choose appropriate subordination and coordination by locating problem sentences and revising them.

VISITING THE BIG APPLE

(1) The train comes to a halt at Grand Central Station, and masses of people push their way through the opened door. (2) As the women hold tightly to their purses and as the businessmen clutch their briefcases, they move forward. (3) The world changes abruptly as one walks through the revolving door of the station onto the crowded streets of Manhattan. (4) For the visitor it is a burst of color, filled with excitement and glamour.

(5) The first thing to notice as you walk down the streets are the buildings surrounding you. (6) They are like a maze, and no matter where you go, they are peering down on you. (7) They are tightly designed to be next to each other, and each one has its own look and style. (8) Next you notice the traffic. (9) As soon as you enter a car or need to walk across the street, you are in a race. (10) As cars speed to try to beat the red light, clouds of exhaust fumes fill the air. (11) You hear a screech, and somebody slams on his brakes, and a bicyclist passes by. (12) The driver curses but immediately speeds on ahead and tries to beat out the other traffic. (Student writer)

The numbers of the sentences to be revised: _____

_____

Revisions of these sentences:

_____

_____

_____

_____

_____

_____

_____

_____

_____

_____

Exercise 4

Find a paragraph that you wrote before you learned how sentences can be expanded and combined. What is the purpose of that paragraph? Revise the sentences by combining and expanding them to fit your purpose.

Old version:

_____

_____

_____

_____

_____

_____

_____

_____

Revised version:

_____

_____

_____

_____

_____

_____

_____

_____

_____

TYPES OF SENTENCES AND THEIR EFFECTS

Exercise 1

Analyze the four selections included here and identify them as standard, balanced, or periodic sentences. For each sentence in each selection, write the appropriate abbreviation in the space provided.

S = Standard (a sentence with a subject and predicate)
B = Balanced (a sentence with two parallel structures set off against each other)
P = Periodic (a sentence that builds up, often through two or three parallel constructions, to a climactic statement in the final main clause)

Type of
Sentence

1. _____   Once, the American automobile, built on an assembly line invented and perfected by Americans, was the quintessential symbol of this country's know-how, a vital part of its industrial foundation. It provided the jobs and the wheels to carry generations of automotive workers and other Americans to an improved middle-class life, surely better than that of their parents but

2. _____   not as good as that of their children. Many Middle Western cities were built around the auto industry—steel, rubber, parts, machine tools and other related businesses, whose readily available jobs and certain overtime were the

3. _____   lure for workers leaving the countryside. Buying a new car every two or three years was as common as 4 percent mortgages and 24-cents-a-gallon

4. _____   gasoline.

      As late as 1978, some 11.3 million automobiles, American and foreign,

5. _____   were sold in the United States. But then the Shah of Iran fell, uncertainty

6. _____   enfolded the oil resources of the Middle East and the gas lines doubled. Auto sales slipped and by 1982 came to slightly under 8 million, with no

7. _____   signs of growth. . . .

      Volume sales, once the be-all and end-all of any dealership, still matter;

8. _____   but of increasing import is the carefully monitored profit per car. Given today's high operating costs—not to mention high risks—selling a lot of cars does not guarantee financial success if the computer says the profit is inade-

9. _____   quate. It is a lesson learned the hard way by 4,400 of the nation's 30,100 franchised new-car dealers who since 1973 have gone the way of huge tail

10. _____   fins. (Excerpt from Andrew H. Malcolm, "Hard Sell in the Showroom," *New York Times Magazine*)

Type of
Sentence

1. _____   The fire in room 404 started the way many do, with a cigarette igniting an upholstered chair. The occupants of the room escaped unharmed, but 12 other guests at Houston's Westchase Hilton Hotel died from the fire that

2. _____   night in March 1982 even though flames never spread beyond room 404. Like almost 6,000 Americans who die each year in fires, they were victims

3. _____   of smoke, not flames.

      In fact, 80 percent of fire deaths are the result of smoke inhalation, but

4. _____   researchers have a lot of questions about what it is in smoke that kills. . . . The puzzle is that carbon monoxide, the supposed villain, turns out not to

5. _____   be. At least not alone. Carbon monoxide is an odorless, colorless gas given

6. _____   off by nearly everything that burns; when inhaled, it binds with red blood

7. _____   cells, preventing them from carrying vital oxygen to the body's cells. In the

8. ____ Houston fire only two of the 12 victims had anything close to lethal doses of carbon monoxide in their blood. (Excerpt from Stephen Budiansky, "How Does Smoke Kill?" *Science 83*)

Type of
Sentence

1. ____
2. ____

I feel lost in Berlin. It has no resemblance to the city I had supposed it was. There once was a Berlin which I would have known, from descriptions in books—the Berlin of the last century and the beginning of the present one: a dingy city in a marsh, with rough streets, muddy and lantern-lighted, dividing straight rows of ugly houses all alike, compacted into blocks as square and plain and uniform and monotonous and serious as so many dry-

3. ____
4. ____
5. ____
6. ____
7. ____
8. ____
9. ____

goods boxes. But that Berlin has disappeared. It seems to have disappeared totally, and left no sign. The bulk of the Berlin of to-day has about it no suggestion of a former period. The site it stands on has traditions and a history, but the city itself has no traditions and no history. It is a new city; the newest I have ever seen. Chicago would seem venerable beside it; for there are many old-looking districts in Chicago, but not many in Berlin. The main mass of the city looks as if it had been built last week, the rest of it has a just perceptibly graver tone, and looks as if it might be six or even

10. ____

eight months old. (Excerpt from Mark Twain, "The German Chicago," in *The Complete Essays of Mark Twain*, edited by Charles Neider)

Type of
Sentence

1. ____

Since the days of ancient Greece, educators have realized that the ideal learning situation is the one student to one teacher ratio. European aristo-crats traditionally gave their children the privilege of this one-to-one instruc-

2. ____
3. ____

tion. Students attending famous English universities such as Oxford and Cambridge also enjoyed this privilege and continue to do so today. There are few American schoolchildren, however, who are able to enjoy the bene-

4. ____

fits of individualized instruction.

5. ____

The reason for the lack of one-to-one instruction in American schools is that the United States is committed to the education of all children. The Constitution guarantees this, and as a result, there are far more students

6. ____

than there are teachers. Also, few college-age students in America can af-ford to attend a private college where the student-teacher ratio is small, and they wind up attending a state-funded college where the teacher-stu-dent ratio is so large that students often have courses with teachers they

7. ____

never talk to. (Student writer)

Exercise 2

In the three selections included below, find the parallel structures used by these authors and then consider the reasons for using this type of sentence. What is the effect of these parallel structures? Do they further the writer's purpose?

> At this stage of my story, Israel is not the same society whose rise from a vulnerable birth I have followed from the earliest days. It has lost its rhapsodic sense. It is an anxious people, consumed by fear of the immense growth in Arab power; fear of erosion in American support; fear of its incapacity to achieve a stable economic order; fear of the long-term effects of a loss of magnetism, reflected in a dwindling immigration and a disquieting flight of manpower from the country. The lucid, visionary but empirical doctrine of the Labor movement is in eclipse. I believe that the popular reaction against a party too long in power is not the final answer, and that Israel will regain the balanced view by which she has of creativity. Some writers have defined anxiety as the essence of the Jewish condition. The question is whether we shall make our anxiety fertile or whether we shall squander it in self-pity and despair. (Excerpt from Abba Eban, *An Autobiography*)

How does the parallelism in this writer's sentences further his purpose?

_____

_____

_____

_____

> At San Francisco State College on that particular morning the wind was blowing the cold rain in squalls across the muddied lawns and against the lighted windows of empty classrooms. In the days before there had been fires set and classes invaded and finally a confrontation with the San Francisco Police Tactical Unit, and in the weeks to come the campus would become what many people on it were pleased to call "a battlefield." The police and the Mace and the noon arrests would become the routine of life on the campus, and every night the combatants would review their day on television: the waves of students advancing, the commotion at the edge of the frame, the riot sticks flashing, the instant of jerky camera that served to suggest at what risk the film was obtained; then a cut to the weather map. (Excerpt from Joan Didion, "The White Album," *The White Album*)

How does the parallelism in this writer's sentences further her purpose?

_____

_____

_____

_____

There is perhaps, for all concerned, no period of life so unpleasant, so unappealing, so downright unpalatable, as that of adolescence. And while pretty much everyone who comes into contact with him is disagreeably affected, certainly no one is in for a ruder shock than the actual teenager himself. Fresh from twelve straight years of uninterrupted cuteness, he is singularly unprepared to deal with the harsh consequences of inadequate appearance. Almost immediately upon entering the thirteenth year of life, a chubby little child becomes a big fat girl, and a boy previously spoken of as "small for his age" finds that he is, in reality, a boy who is short.

Problems of physical beauty, grave though they be, are not all that beset the unwary teen. Philosophical, spiritual, social, legal—a veritable multitude of difficulties daily confront him. Understandably disconcerted, the teenager almost invariably finds himself in a state of unrelenting misery. This is, of course, unfortunate, even lamentable. Yet one frequently discovers a lack of sympathy for the troubled youth. This dearth of compassion is undoubtedly due to the teenager's insistence upon dealing with his lot in an unduly boisterous fashion. He is, quite simply, at an age where he can keep nothing to himself. No impulse too fleeting, no sentiment too raw, that the teenager does not feel compelled to share it with those around him. (Excerpt from Fran Lebowitz, "Tips for Teens," *Social Studies*)

How does the parallelism in this writer's sentences further her purpose?

_____

_____

_____

_____

Exercise 3

Using the information provided here, write three balanced sentences that point up the contrast between the things being compared.

1. The number of Americans over 65 is increasing. They are probably the fastest growing age group in the country. Nearly 40 percent of the people in this group suffer from some chronic physical or mental handicap. Because of social and economic changes, families are now less able to support elderly relatives, and American medical and social service systems are woefully unprepared to help all these people.

   Your sentence: _____

   _____

   _____

2. In the instrument panels on new cars, the Japanese trend is to more digital read-outs and graphics in front of the driver. In the European cars the instrument panel continues to use gauges and dials. Critics say the Japanese trend is too gimmicky and the European way is too conservative.

   Your sentence: _____

   _____

   _____

3. In America psychiatric treatment has become acceptable enough for people with emotional distress to seek it out. An American psychiatrist recently returned from a visit to the USSR and states that the need for psychiatric care in the Soviet Union is still seen as a cause for shame.

   Your sentence: _____

   _____

   _____

   _____

Exercise 4

Construct a periodic sentence for each of the formulas given here. If possible, work with several other writers to create your examples.

1. Formula: Unless A, unless B, unless C, D will happen.

   Your periodic sentence: _____

   _____

   _____

   _____

2. Formula: Having accomplished A, I finally achieved B.

   Your periodic sentence: _____

   _____

   _____

   _____

3. Formula: With A in mind and with B in mind, I realized C.

   Your periodic sentence: _____

   _____

   _____

   _____

4. Formula: If A, if B, if C, then D.

   Your periodic sentence: _____

   _____

   _____

   _____

5. Formula: Unlike A, which is . . . , and unlike B, which is . . . , C is . . . .

Your periodic sentence: _____

_____

_____

_____

REVISING SENTENCES

Clarity

Exercise 1

Some writing lacks clarity because the sentences are overloaded with information. The two examples below are taken from a U.S. government document that tells companies how to bid for government projects. The sentences should be divided into shorter sentences. Draw a vertical line after each part of the sentence that could be rewritten as a shorter, clearer sentence. If possible, do this exercise together with several other writers.

> You should thoroughly familiarize yourself with this clause and with the related rules and regulations of the Secretary of Labor on equal employment opportunity since in submitting a bid you agree to certain specific responsibilities in the area of nondiscrimination in employment which may include submission of certain reports prior to and/or after award and the development and maintenance of a written affirmative action program to assure equal employment opportunity at each of your establishments.

> This contract may be extended for a period of one year at the option of the Government, by the Contracting Officer giving written notice of the Government's exercise of such option to the contractor not later than the last day of the term of the contract; provided that such notice shall have no effect if given less than 60 days prior to the last day of the term of the contract unless the Contracting Officer has given preliminary written notice of an intent to exercise such option at least sixty (60) days prior to the last day of the term of the contract (such preliminary notice shall not be construed as an exercise of the option, and will not bind the Government to exercise the option).

Find another example of an overly long, unclear sentence and copy it or clip it to this page. Government documents are a likely source.

_____

_____

_____

_____

_____

_____

Exercise 2

Another source of unclear writing is the overly short or ambiguous newspaper headline. Can you pinpoint possible sources of confusion in these headlines?

1. GRADUATION REQUIREMENTS RAISED BY SCHOOL OFFICIALS

   Possible confusion: _____

   _____

   _____

   _____

2. TELEVISION GRABS AUDIENCE MAJORITY

   Possible confusion: _____

   _____

   _____

3. CONGRESS REPORTS, SERVICES CUT

   Possible confusion: _____

   _____

   _____

4. A TEAM DEFEATED

   Possible confusion: _____

   _____

   _____

5. GOVERNOR: NEW RATE SYSTEM UNDER HIM

   Possible confusion: _____

   _____

   _____

6. CLEAN-UP GROUP CHARGES FRAUD, DEMANDS INVESTIGA-
   TION, COUNCIL DENIES IT

   Possible confusion: _____

   _____

   _____

   Find three examples of unclear headlines and copy them here:

1. _____

2. _____

3. _____

Exercise 3

The following sentences, written by students, lack clarity because of unclear pronouns, incorrect punctuation, and confusing sentence structure.
Revise the sentences so that they are clearer. Since the sentences weren't
clear as written, you will have to decide what meaning you want each sentence to convey.

1. After the bike slammed into the motorcycle parked at the curb, its wheels were still spinning for several minutes.

   Revision: _____

   _____

2. A better rapport would exist between students and teachers if they weren't so concerned with grades.

   Revision: _____

   _____

3. Having eaten the animal stretched in the sunshine and began to lick its paws.

   Revision: _____

   _____

4. We stayed in a really nice mobile home that rested in a little motel court surrounded by shade trees. This made our vacation very pleasant.

   Revision: _____

   _____

5. These two solutions to the problem that I saw in high school may not work, but it is better than just letting the problems go on without any action.

   Revision: _____

   _____

   _____

6. If at the beginning of the story the peasants had talked to Kutcherov and Elena, they might not have left.

Revision: _____

_____

_____

7. Thus I believe that a college education should mainly provide a student with an education related to his or her choice of career rather than generalizing in studies he may never use again in his life or won't be of any value in finding a job which demands more specific knowledge of an individual.

Revision: _____

_____

_____

8. I feel that violence is so prevalent on TV today because people are intrigued by it, and this reflects what is happening in society today.

Revision: _____

_____

_____

Emphasis

Exercise 1

As you read the two selections that follow, notice where the important elements of each sentence are. Are they at the beginning, in the middle, or at the end? Put a 1 over the most important element and a 2 over the next most important element.

The power of the N.S.A. [National Security Agency], whose annual budget and staff are believed to exceed those of either the F.B.I. or the C.I.A., is enhanced by its unique legal status within the Federal Government.

Unlike the Agriculture Department, the Postal Service or even the C.I.A., the N.S.A. has no specific Congressional law defining its responsibilities and obligations. Instead, the agency, based at Fort George Meade, about 20 miles northeast of Washington, has operated under a series of Presidential directives. Because of Congress's failure to draft a law for the agency, because of the tremendous secrecy surrounding the N.S.A.'s work and because of the highly technical and thus thwarting character of its equipment, the N.S.A. is free to define and pursue its own goals. (Excerpt from David Burnham, "The Silent Power of the N.S.A.," *New York Times Magazine*)

Career prospects for Japanese women are steadily improving. In recent years, largely because a declining birthrate has created a shortage of new male entrants into the labor force, there has been a sizable influx of women into the highly technical field of computer programming. Some of the most prestigious Japanese Government agencies now routinely include at least a few women when they hire recent university graduates earmarked for the upper reaches of the bureaucracy. And a growing number of women in their 30's and 40's now hold influential positions in retailing and the service industries—a matter of particular significance since these are among the fastest-growing sectors of the Japanese economy. (Excerpt from Robert C. Christopher, "Changing Face of Japan," *The New York Times Magazine*)

Exercise 2

Sentences in each of the examples below use emphatic repetition. Study the pattern of these sentences and then use that same pattern in sentences of your own.

1. The Brooklyn Bridge holds a special place in America's imagination; we have written songs about it, photographed it, sketched it, painted it, etched it on glass, and embroidered it on pillows.

   Your sentence: _____

   _____

   _____

   _____

2. Breakthroughs in eradicating heart disease have come on a dozen fronts, from diet to diagnosis, from medicine to machines, from transplants to tomography.

   Your sentence: _____

   _____

   _____

   _____

3. Until quite recently academic study of Vietnam was almost nonexistent. "A survey by the *New York Times* in 1970 found that there was no scholar in the United States who devoted most of his or her time to studying North Vietnam; there was no American university with a tenured professorship in Vietnamese studies, and there were fewer than 30 students in the country studying the Vietnam language." (Fox Butterfield, "The New Vietnam Scholarship," *The New York Times Magazine*)

   Your sentence: _____

   _____

   _____

   _____

4. The nearest most of us get to real contemplation is when we watch a good sports contest. Here we are near what is best in ourselves, for we are spectators not for any selfish reason, not for anything we might get out of the game, not for money or exercise, and not for glory, but just because the game is there and because we lose ourselves in its playing.

Your sentence: _____

_____

_____

_____

Economy

Exercise 1

The sentences included here all contain unnecessary words. If possible, work in a small group with several other writers and cut out every word that you can while retaining the meaning of the sentence. Assume that you will be sending your revised sentence as a telegram or night letter and you will be charged five cents a word. What is the total cost of each of your sentences? Compare your costs with those of another group working on this exercise to see who produces the less expensive versions.

1. A good manager, as everyone knows, is one who is able to express his thoughts and to express the decisions he makes clearly, briefly, and in a pleasant manner.

Your version: _____

_____

_____

Cost: _____

2. It seems to me that most people tend to prefer living in areas where there is a very low crime rate and where the annual yearly percentage of sunny days is higher than at least 70 percent.

Your version: _____

_____

_____

Cost: _____

3. Looking at the subject of homework, I think that it is really not very effective to assign a large number of homework problems in my physics course because with the large number to do, a student falls further and further behind in reading the textbook and in doing other work necessary to prepare for the course which is quite difficult as is.

Your version: _____

_____

_____

Cost: _____

4. There has been considerable concern about the level of employee unhappiness within the company lately judging from the increasing number of complaints made in recent weeks.

Your version: _____

_____

_____

Cost: _____

5. The drying process is a process in which the fruit is baked in very hot ovens of 500° in order to remove excess moisture which is in the fruit.

Your version: _____

_____

_____

Cost: _____

6. There has been considerable concern expressed lately by the coach about the effectiveness of the new weight-lifting exercises which were recently added to the workout schedule that is assigned to everyone.

Your version: _____

_____

_____

Cost: _____

Exercise 2

Gather two examples of highly economical prose. Examine merchandise or seed catalogs, movie or TV program summaries, brief instructions for public services (such as a phone booth or 24-hour automatic banking service), or any similar set of concise instructions. Clip or copy your examples here.

1. _____

_____

_____

_____

2. _____

_____

_____

_____

Exercise 3

To be sure that you recognize artificially inflated prose, rewrite a few sentences so that they are excessively wordy. Using the suggestions listed here, add as many words as you can to the sentences that follow.

Suggestions for inflating sentences:

a. Use the following words and phrases.
   seems, seems to
   tends, tends to
   begins, begins to
   happens, happens to
   it seems to be that
   I feel that
   in my opinion
   it occurs to me that
   in order to
b. Use a large number of pronouns.
   who
   which
   that
c. Introduce ideas with empty phrases.
   there is
   there are
   in this instance
   this is a case of
   the reason for this is that
d. Add qualifiers.
   sort of
   kind of
   actually
   really
e. Be redundant.
   not 9 p.m., but 9 p.m. at night
   not the beginning, but the first beginning
   not the conclusion, but the final conclusion

1. Most children like candy.

   _____

   _____

2. The meeting will be held at 10 a.m.

   _____

_____

_____

3. The boring movie ran for 2½ hours.

_____

_____

4. The rodeo arena was longer than a football field.

_____

_____

5. Last night, before the swim meet, I was nervous.

_____

_____

_____

Find examples from advertising copy and slogans to inflate. For example, a diet center advises readers to "weight no longer," a cigarette ad states, "America's best," and a car company says, "We are driven." Find similar concise slogans and inflate them.

6. _____

_____

7. _____

_____

_____

8. _____

_____

_____

9. _____

_____

_____

10. _____

_____

_____

Variety

Exercise 1

Included here are pairs of sentences that can be combined into one sentence and ordered in several ways. Write two different versions of each sentence by rearranging the order, embedding one sentence inside the other, or making one a clause or phrase that depends on the other.

Example: The example failed because of Murphy's Law. Murphy's Law states that buttered bread always falls buttered side down.
Version 1: The experiment failed because of Murphy's Law, which states that buttered bread always falls buttered side down.
Version 2: Due to Murphy's Law, which states that buttered bread always falls buttered side down, the experiment failed.

1. I plan to visit San Francisco this summer.
San Francisco has a wide variety of tourist attractions.

Version 1: _____

_____

_____

Version 2: _____

_____

_____

2. The highjackers wanted to attract the attention of the American public. The highjackers ordered the plane to fly to Morocco.

Version 1: _____

_____

_____

Version 2: _____

_____

_____

3. He was driving without a license. He ran a red light and was arrested by the sheriff.

Version 1: _____

_____

_____

Version 2: _____

_____

_____

4. William stared at the music in front of him. His fingers rested lightly on the piano keys.

Version 1: _____

_____

Version 2: _____

_____

_____

ORIGINAL SENTENCES FOR EXERCISE 2 IN
"THE RELATION OF COMBINATION TO PURPOSE "

1. "The architect I. M. Pei, creator of the East Building of the National Gallery in Washington, the New York City Convention and Exhibition Center and some of the most conspicuous skyscrapers of the last decade, does not normally design relatively modest 325-room, low-rise hotels." (Excerpt from Paul Goldberger, "I. M. Pei Rediscovers China," *New York Times Magazine*)
2. "A storm recently ripped through California's Altamont Pass, where several hundred windmills have been installed to capture the energy in the powerful winds that whistle through the area." (Excerpt from C. P. Gilmore, "PS/What's New," *Popular Science*)
3. "A friend of mine, writing in another magazine, argues that America is rife with snobbery and obsessed with status, and offers as evidence the fact that people will pay extra for a shirt with a little alligator sewn on it." (Excerpt from Michael Kinsley, "Dressing Down," *Harper's*)
4. "When I first heard of it, I could hardly believe it—that after the garbage is collected twice a week in the city of Tucson, some of those plastic bags are opened and the contents painstakingly examined, classified, weighed, and recorded by students from the University of Arizona." (Excerpt from Peter T. White, "The Fascinating World of Trash," *National Geographic*)
5. "The chief vestige of free enterprise permitted openly in the Soviet Union is the millions of private plots that provide perhaps a quarter of the food consumed by the 270 million Soviet citizens." (Excerpt from Lawrence Minard and James W. Michaels, "Why Workers Won't Work in the Soviet Union," *Forbes*)

8
Diction

DENOTATION AND CONNOTATION

Exercise 1

The connotation of some words—or the attitudes we associate with them—can easily be seen when we examine pairs of words that are essentially similar in meaning, but different in the favorable or unfavorable attitudes they evoke in most people. Listed below are ten pairs of words that evoke negative or positive feelings. For each pair place a plus sign (+) after the word that conveys a more favorable attitude and a minus sign (–) after the word that carries a less favorable attitude.

	+ or – ?		+ or – ?
1. refreshing	_____	6. cop	_____
chilly	_____	officer of the law	_____
2. plain	_____	7. skinny	_____
natural	_____	slender	_____
3. clever	_____	8. statesman	_____
sly	_____	politico	_____
4. chuckle	_____	9. smile	_____
giggle	_____	smirk	_____
5. highbrow	_____	10. domineering	_____
cultured	_____	strong willed	_____

233

Exercise 2

In the space below list six words that you think have favorable connotations and six that have unfavorable connotations. These do not have to be pairs. Do not indicate which are positive and which are negative and be sure to mix up the list so that not all the favorable words are together. Then, read your list to another writer or to a small group of writers in your class and ask your audience to rate each word with a plus or a minus sign. Listen for possible disagreements.

Your list   Rating

1. _____   _____
2. _____   _____
3. _____   _____
4. _____   _____
5. _____   _____
6. _____   _____
7. _____   _____
8. _____   _____
9. _____   _____
10. _____   _____
11. _____   _____
12. _____   _____

How many words did you and your raters agree on? _____

Which words caused disagreement? _____

_____

_____

© 1984 Houghton Mifflin Company

Exercise 3

Practice shifting your viewpoint so that you can describe the same object both favorably and unfavorably. You can do this by first using words with a positive connotation and then switching to words with a negative connotation. If possible, do this exercise with a small group of writers. For the descriptions below, write at least four or five words or phrases that have favorable connotations and another four or five that have unfavorable connotations. For example, you might describe a soft banana as either sweetly ripe or mushy, depending on the desired connotation.

1. Describe a wet street after the rain

   Favorably: _____

   _____

   Unfavorably: _____

   _____

2. Describe a college or professional football team

   Favorably: _____

   _____

   Unfavorably: _____

   _____

3. Characterize a difficult college course

   Favorably: _____

   _____

   Unfavorably: _____

   _____

4. Describe a hamburger made in a fast-food restaurant

   Favorably: _____

   _____

Unfavorably: _____

_____

5. Describe someone who spends a great deal of time practicing one particular sport

Favorably: _____

_____

Unfavorably: _____

_____

6. Describe a new regulation for student parking on campus

Favorably: _____

_____

Unfavorably: _____

_____

7. Describe a group of three or four teen-age girls walking down the street together

Favorably: _____

_____

Unfavorably: _____

_____

8. Describe a recent movie or television program

Favorably: _____

_____

Unfavorably: _____

_____

9. Describe a window display in a store.

Favorably: _____

_____

Unfavorably: _____

_____

10. Describe a particular newscaster or sports announcer

Favorably: _____

_____

Unfavorably: _____

_____

Exercise 4

Working with a small group of other writers, make up a list of words that characterize a person who is intoxicated. Try to think of at least five or six words.

1. _____

2. _____

3. _____

4. _____

5. _____

6. _____

Using your list, arrange the words along a spectrum from negative to positive.

_____

(most negative word)   (most positive word)

THREE QUALITIES OF GOOD DICTION

Appropriateness

Formal and Informal

In order to determine how formal or informal writing should be, writers have to analyze both the situation and the audience for which the writing is intended. Then, they can decide on the degree of formality needed. The two situations explained here offer you the opportunity to practice this kind of analysis. In both cases you have to write to someone to ask for information.

1. You need to write to a cousin who lives in a city several hundred miles away. You have heard that this city will be the site of a convention for people who collect and trade old comic books. You would like to go to the convention, but you need to know when and where it will be held. Your cousin is about five years older than you are. Although you haven't seen her for over a year, the two of you are generally fairly close. Write to ask if she can find the information you need.

    Analysis of audience and situation: _____

    _____

    _____

    Write a short request based on this analysis: _____

    _____

    _____

    _____

    _____

    _____

    _____

    _____

2. You want to inquire about a summer job selling local advertisements
for *The Daily Courier* the second largest newspaper in the state, but
you don't know when or how to apply. Your uncle belongs to the same
physical fitness club as the personnel director, Mrs. Clark, with whom
he has become quite friendly. He says that she is so overworked that
she probably doesn't answer every letter she gets unless it really catches
her attention. Since you've had great success selling personalized
T-shirts from a catalog, you know you can be equally successful for
The Daily Courier if you can only get Mrs. Clark to give you the information you need. However, you can't be gimmicky since you also want
your letter to look like a professional business communication. Write to
Mrs. Clark.

Analysis of audience and situation: _____

_____

_____

Write a short request based on this analysis: _____

_____

_____

_____

_____

_____

_____

_____

_____

_____

_____

Learned and Popular Words

Exercise 1

To practice recognizing both learned and popular words, read the two selections below and list three learned words and three popular words in each.

> We were not really the Midwest, my father explained; that would be Iowa or Nebraska, Kansas—hopeless places. We were the Upper Midwest, as the weatherman said, elevating us above the dreary mean. My father pointed with derision at the cars with Iowa license plates, hauling boats on trailers behind them, as we passed them on Highway 200 going north. "Will you look at that," he said. "Those Iowa people have to lug that boat all the way up here." My brother and I looked at the dummies in the Iowa car as we passed. "They're crazy to get to the water, they'll even fish in the middle of the day," he said, as if the Iowa Bedouins were so water mad that a school of walleye could toy with them in the noon heat, while my father coolly appeared at dawn and twilight to make the easy Minnesota-savvy kill. He pointed out to us, over and over, the folly of the Iowans and their pathetic pursuit of standing water. (Patricia Hampl, *A Romantic Education*)

Learned Words	Popular Words
1. _____	1. _____
2. _____	2. _____
3. _____	3. _____

> If John F. Kennedy did rather little in his brief term as President, his presence enabled others to do more. Though he had none of Franklin D. Roosevelt's talent for mobilizing popular constituencies, Kennedy was admired by the liberal intelligentsia quite as much as Adlai Stevenson had been a few years earlier. To literate Americans, a literate President seems a luxury beyond words. What Kennedy gave us was a glimmer of imagination and style. The glimmer helped. People bored with the flaccidity of the Eisenhower years, students recognizing they could now experiment with new ways of living, blacks looking for some national figure to bless their new militancy—all, you might say, made Kennedy into an emblem of their hopes. And went further than he ever would have. ("The Decade That Failed," *New York Times Magazine*)

© 1984 Houghton Mifflin Company

Learned Words	Popular Words

1. _____   1. _____

2. _____   2. _____

3. _____   3. _____

Exercise 2

To add to your vocabulary of learned words, use a thesaurus to find an equivalent learned word for each of the following common words.

1. wordy: _____

2. knowable: _____

3. agree: _____

4. important: _____

5. a ball: _____

6. favorable: _____

7. to stagger: _____

8. to love: _____

9. sneaky: _____

10. excess: _____

Exercise 3

In each of these sentences choose between the two possibilities in parentheses by selecting the one most appropriate to the sentence.

1. The lawyer's statement accused the defendant of (goofing up, misrepresenting) the facts.

2. I tried to explain to my friend that I was (confused, discountenanced) by the directions he gave me for finding his house.
3. The notice to the employees stated that the recent expansion plans would have to be (dumped, canceled) because of lack of funds.
4. Will you (commence, begin) your new job next week?
5. The conservation group accused the logging company of (depleting, messing up) the forest.
6. At the (end, termination) of the concert, we all applauded heartily.
7. The statement of support issued by the newspaper's editor was (encouraging, a shot in the arm).
8. The (substantial, big) increase in sales helped the company to maintain the price of its stock.
9. The candidate's speech (galvanized, turned on) the audience and provoked enthusiastic applause.
10. The diplomats (hit it off, achieved an agreement) on trade concessions after several discussions.
11. The cookbook directions state that the butter is to be left out until it is (malleable, soft).

Colloquialisms

Take this workbook to a place where you are likely to hear conversational speech. For example, go to a college dorm, fast-food restaurant, video arcade, bowling alley, gym, or student lounge. Listen to the speech of the people around you and write down a sampling of what you hear. Try to record at least four or five sentences. Then, analyze the speech and select five words or phrases that you would characterize as colloquial and inappropriate for formal writing.

Record what you heard here: _____

_____

_____

_____

_____

_____

_____

_____

_____

Colloquial words or phrases: _____

_____

_____

_____

Several colloquialisms in the student essay below should be eliminated. Underline the words you find too colloquial for the essay and suggest better choices above the words you have underlined.

Glancing through the newspaper help wanted ads can be a real pain if you don't know what you want to do for a summer job. In my case, a newspaper ad led me to the least favorite job I have ever had, hoeing weeds.

Arriving at the O'Neal farm at about eight o'clock each morning started my day off. After wasting about half an hour while I was sharpening my hoe real slow, I found that this only took up a small fraction of an eight-hour day. Then I had to drive a beat-up Fill truck out to the vegetable field, which was a real hassle because the truck didn't want to behave. Pulling up beside the field to be hoed that day and glancing out over the field can give you a real heart attack because of all the weeds that have to come out. The rest of the day was like a continuous broken record. (Student writer)

Slang

1. List a few current slang words that refer to money, to people who are not well liked, and to things or ideas that are good or favorable: _____

   _____

   _____

   _____

2. Some slang is a collection of words used by a particular group. Think of two groups who are likely to have their own special vocabularies of slang words, groups such as musicians, athletes, actors, and so on. Gather some of their slang words either by interviewing a member of the group or watching a television program in which a member is interviewed.

   a. Type of group: _____

      Slang words used: _____

      _____

      _____

      _____

   b. Type of group: _____

      Slang words used: _____

      _____

      _____

3. Some slang becomes dated and dies. To compile a list of some now-forgotten or infrequently used slang terms, interview a person who is at least forty-five years old. Ask that person what slang terms were popular during his or her teen-age years. Try to identify terms for dating, for being attractive, for being popular, for being well dressed, and so on. Write down at least ten of those slang words.

a. _____   f. _____

b. _____   g. _____

c. _____   h. _____

d. _____   i. _____

e. _____   j. _____

Using the slang terms listed above, write a few sentences giving advice on how to win friends and be popular.

_____

_____

_____

_____

_____

Rewrite the sentences above using today's slang.

_____

_____

_____

_____

4. Slang words do not always communicate clearly because people's definitions sometimes differ. To see whether this is true for words in your vocabulary, list five slang terms you frequently use:

a. _____

_____

b. _____

_____

c. _____

_____

d. _____

_____

e. _____

_____

Read this list to another student or small group in your class and ask your audience for as precise a definition as possible. Record the definition next to your word. How many of the definitions correspond to your use of the term?

Specificity

Exercise 1

For this project, work with another writer or a small group of writers. Select a movie, TV show, sporting event, record, play, book, or concert that you've all seen or heard. Decide on a general statement that you would all agree on. For example, you might choose a general statement such as the following:

1. <u>(name of a play)</u> was well acted.
2. <u>(football team)</u> lacks any star players.
3. <u>(name of a movie)</u> showed too much violence.

Write down the general statement and then generate a list of specific words, examples, or details to make the sentence refer to that particular movie or play and not some movie or play in general. Then, revise your general statement by making it more specific.

General statement: _____

_____

Specifics: _____

_____

_____

_____

Revised statement: _____

_____

_____

Exercise 2

The need for specifics is particularly apparent in certain kinds of work. Think of someone who must gather specifics and not general statements. This person might be a policeman at the scene of a crime, an insurance investigator assessing damage, a scientist in the laboratory recording what he or she observes, a psychologist interpreting a patient's dreams. Interview that person about the kinds of problems that arise when the information gathered is not sufficiently specific.

Person interviewed: _____

Your report: _____

_____

_____

_____

_____

_____

Exercise 3

In each of the sentences below underline the subject and object words that refer to a general class. In each case substitute a more specific term and, if possible, also add a descriptive word or phrase.

1. A man went into a building.

   Revised version: _____

   _____

   _____

2. The animal ate its food.

   Revised version: _____

   _____

   _____

3. The parent held the child.

   Revised version: _____

   _____

   _____

4. The store sells candy.

   Revised version: _____

   _____

   _____

5. The car hit an object.

   Revised version: _____

   _____

   _____

Exercise 4

In each sentence below, the italicized word or phrase weakens the sentence because it is too general or abstract. For each italicized word write a better word or phrase, one that is more concrete or specific, on the line to the right.

1. Scared by the shrill, high-pitched *sound* coming from the robot, the toddler burst into tears. _____
2. Standing on the sunlit river bank, he watched the water *flow* over and around the shining black rocks. _____
3. It was one of those awkward moments in life when you know you are about to do something *wrong*. _____
4. His sleek sportscar *drove quietly* at high speeds. _____
5. The fashionably dressed models in the elegant store window were standing in *unusual positions*. _____

Exercise 5

In Example 1 below, the writer revised her sentence to make it more specific. Examine the way she achieved this specificity and use the same strategies to make Example 2 more specific.

Example 1: When I was younger, television influenced me because I tried to imitate the people I saw on TV and tried to take the advice I heard in the ads.

Example 1 revised: Until about five years ago television influenced me greatly. I tried to imitate the little girls on "Kindergarten College," and I lost fifteen pounds and a considerable amount of money on beauty aids to try to imitate the clean, natural look of Cheryl Tiegs and the other models on TV.

Example 2: High school is different from college because in high school I didn't have any responsibilities at home, but now I have to take care of myself. Now I have to do things my mom took care of at home.

Example 2 revised: _____

_____

_____

_____

_____

_____

_____

Exercise 6

In the two selections from student essays included here, the writers' descriptions need more concrete words—words that refer to things that can be perceived by the senses. Read the paragraphs and then try to help the writers by suggesting more concrete terms and phrases. You may want to check the list of descriptive words in your textbook to help you think of better options for these writers. Write your suggestions above the words that are not sufficiently concrete.

Another trademark of autumn is, of course, the weather. Fall means a mixture of climates that are almost constantly changing and therefore never leaves time for the boredom and consistency found in other seasons. Early fall means hot, humid days that are great for swimming and sunbathing. These days last only a short while until cooler days start taking over. These days I like best of all because I love cool, breezy days with the smell of burning leaves in our back yard. It is also ideal weather to put on a jacket and take a walk through the park or watch a football game. But soon after the days start getting colder, one might even find himself caught in an early snowfall. (Student writer)

A few weeks ago I attended the Buddy Rich–Rich Little show at the Concert Hall. The band played some very good music; Rich Little's impressions were great. The entire show was very enjoyable and pleasing. When I left the Concert Hall I felt good, and I am sure most of the other people there did too. One word that can sum up this show and the happy feelings it brought is "entertainment." (Student writer)

Imagery

Exercise 1

To help you sharpen your ability to create similes and metaphors, this exercise offers you some practice in joining dissimilar objects and ideas. First, go somewhere and write down twenty nouns, verbs, and adjectives that the place brings to mind. This will be List 1. Then, go to another place which is very different and make a similar list for that place, List 2. When you have done this, practice combining a word or concept from List 1 with a word or concept from List 2. Some of the results will not seem effective or interesting, but don't reject anything that comes to mind. When you have paired six or eight items, look back over your list of images. Most likely, you will find that one or two of those images will be original or thought-provoking. Even if you don't like any of the results, you will have gained practice in joining dissimilar objects and ideas, a thought process that will help you to create effective imagery in writing.

To see how this works, look at this short example:

Place A: a kitchen   Place B: a lecture hall

List 1: warmth   List 2: students
    hanging plants   rows of seats
    shelves with tin cans of food   ceiling lights
    cutting and chopping   seriousness
    whiteness   squeaking chalk

Possible combination: students stacked in rows like tin cans in a cupboard

You try it:

Place A: _____   Place B: _____

List 1: _____   List 2: _____

_____   _____

_____   _____

_____   _____

_____   _____

Possible combinations: _____

_____

_____

_____

_____

_____

Exercise 2

In the two selections from student essays included here, both writers use imagery in their descriptions. How effective is it? Read both selections and discuss the imagery with another student or with a small group of students in your class. Answer the questions in the evaluation questionnaire.

> What do you think would happen to a pro marathon runner if he didn't run for a year? If he ran again after a year passed by, it would kill him if he finished because he would not be in shape. This is exactly the same with the computer. If a smart person uses a computer to figure answers all the time, he soon forgets how to figure the problem on his own. He has gotten used to plugging numbers in and waiting to have an answer come out. He gets out of shape, and the computer has become his master. If this same person would have used his brain instead of the calculator, he would have been better off. Experts say the average human is like an engine that is idling and not going full power because he uses only twenty percent of his brain to think. (Student writer)

> Five short weeks ago I came to college ready to study eight hours each day to dazzle my professors with my brilliance. But in those five weeks I've barely managed to muster a dull shine. It's difficult to sparkle in a 7:30 a.m. class when you got home only three hours ago.
> I think that the tug-of-war between the busy social life college offers and the need to keep up with my studies, socializing has pulled me too far. All night pizza joints, fraternity parties that never seem to end, and those unplanned trips to nearby colleges drag me away when I should have studied for a chem quiz. Yawning until I am teary-eyed in lecture isn't the way to my professor's heart or grade book. It's time to get down to work and polish my dulled image. (Student writer)

Evaluation Report

1. Names of readers: _____

2. What things were being compared in Selection 1? _____

   _____

   _____

3. What things were being compared in Selection 2? _____

   _____

   _____

4. In which selection is the imagery most original? _____

   _____

5. Which writer used imagery more effectively? _____

   _____

   Why? _____

   _____

6. If you were an editor writing comments to each of the writers, what would you say to each of them about their use of imagery? Try to include both a positive comment on something that was effective and also a suggestion for improvement. Include comments on your personal reaction to the writing as well.

   Comments to the writer of Selection 1: _____

   _____

   _____

   _____

Comments to the writer of Selection 2: _____

_____

_____

_____

REVISING DICTION

Vagueness

In the selection from a student essay included here, the student needs to revise this vague paragraph. But, before he can, he needs to see why the paragraph is vague. Demonstrate its vagueness by offering him at least two or three possible interpretations for each sentence. For example, in sentence 1, the student writes about what he wants to do when he finishes high school. Does he mean something to do in the years ahead, for the summer, or perhaps after the graduation ceremony? Are there other possible interpretations of this sentence? What interpretations can you think of for the other sentences? Work on this exercise with another student or with a small group of students in your class.

> (1) When I was going through high school I had to decide what I wanted to do when I finished. (2) If I picked college, I needed to decide what type of school would be better for me. (3) I decided on a large university because it fit my needs. (4) Finally, quality is also important to me. (Student writer)

Interpretations for sentence 1: _____

_____

_____

_____

Interpretations for sentence 2: _____

_____

_____

_____

Interpretations for sentence 3: _____

_____

_____

_____

Interpretations for sentence 4: _____

_____

_____

_____

Jargon

Exercise 1

Some jargon is composed of learned and technical words used by specialized groups to help them communicate more effectively with each other. List at least four or five groups likely to have their own jargon, groups such as physicists, lawyers, computer programmers, government workers, high-fidelity enthusiasts, and so on.

1. _____

2. _____

3. _____

4. _____

5. _____

Choose at least two of these groups either from the examples given here or from the list you just made. Find five jargon terms used by each of these groups. Some of the words you may know; others you may need to gather from interviews or from reading journals or magazine articles intended for people in these groups.

Group 1: _____
Jargon terms used by this group:

    1. _____

    2. _____

    3. _____

    4. _____

    5. _____

Group 2: _____
Jargon terms used by this group:

    1. _____

    2. _____

    3. _____

    4. _____

    5. _____

Exercise 2

Ineffective or inappropriately used jargon merely inflates ideas that can be expressed more clearly with popular words. We see this kind of unnecessary jargon in the five examples below, which are really familiar old sayings turned into jargon. Read these and translate them back into clear language that we all know.

1. Nothing is of absolute certitude but cessation of life and revenue enhancement.

    Translation: _____

    _____

2. In the presence of gravity, that whose Y coordinate increases in a positive sense will, after the vanishing of its time derivative, have its Y coordinate decrease.

   Translation: _____

   _____

3. Flora of the class Musci within the division Bryophyta are incapable of adhering to extrusive igneous spheroids in motion.

   Translation: _____

   _____

4. In order to eschew the diurnal visitation of a physician, it is imperative to ingest the fruit of the tree *Pyrus malus.*

   Translation: _____

   _____

5. A stipulated event has the probability of occurrence similar to that of the maintenance of a spheroid of frozen H_2O in the nether regions of the condemned.

   Translation: _____

   _____

Now try creating some of these yourself. For suggestions for familiar sayings to jargonize, browse through Bartlett's *Familiar Quotations*, *The Dictionary of Quotations*, *The Home Book of Quotations*, or some other similar collection. Then jargonize the saying by substituting less familiar words for the common ones; a thesaurus or dictionary can help you locate substitutes for common words. If possible, do this as a collaborative effort with another writer or small group of writers in your class.

1. _____

   _____

2. _____

   _____

3. _____

_____

Exercise 3 Instant Jargon

Jargon that is difficult or impossible to understand or is just plain nonsense is easy to create. Think of a three-digit number and then fill in the words from each of the three columns below. For example, if you thought of the number 132, the result is a bit of instant jargon: "responsive guidance situations." Think of your own three-digit numbers and write the phrases that result in the blanks in the paragraph below.

Column 1	Column 2	Column 3
0. total	0. cooperative	0. options
1. responsive	1. digital	1. activities
2. relative	2. policy	2. situations
3. balanced	3. guidance	3. factors
4. functional	4. organizational	4. relationships
5. basic	5. environmental	5. systems
6. group	6. educational	6. capabilities
7. constructive	7. maturity	7. contingencies
8. integrated	8. developmental	8. concepts
9. compatible	9. management	9. programs

Fill in the blanks with your instant jargon:

It was formerly believed that _____

were responsible for the impact of _____

_____ upon _____

and _____. However,

recent studies indicate that _____

_____ and _____ are

of greater significance than _____

in the development of _____.

Can you write a few sentences of your own with the instant jargon you have created from the table above?

_____

_____

_____

_____

_____

_____

(Adapted from *Help! From One to Another*, edited by Carol Bashford Naab)

Triteness

Exercise 1

Collect some clichés by asking people to complete the phrases below with the standard words that come to mind. If you are able to interview people from different age groups, you may find some areas of overlap and some areas of difference.

1. big as _____

2. hot as _____

3. busy as _____

4. work like _____

5. white as _____

6. hungry as _____

7. red as _____

8. sick as _____

9. light as _____

10. pretty as _____

Exercise 2

A different set of clichés and overworked phrases can be found in commercials and ads. Collect at least ten of these trite phrases from TV, magazines, and newspapers. Included below are a few examples to start off your list.

1. new and improved _____

2. a whole new twist _____

3. _____

4. _____

5. _____

6. _____

7. _____

8. _____

9. _____

10. _____

Exercise 3

Clip a short article from a newspaper or magazine. Then, rewrite the article by loading it with clichés instead of the objective phrases used by the reporter. Eric Partridge's *Dictionary of Clichés*, the *Dictionary of Contemporary Usage*, Logan Piersall Smith's *Words and Ideas*, or a similar reference book in the library can suggest stock phrases or clichés to use.

9
Tone and Style

TONE

Informative Versus Affective

Exercise 1

To distinguish between writing that aims at informing and writing that aims at affecting or influencing, read the excerpts included here and determine whether the writer's main purpose is to give you information or to influence your attitudes. In your response, mention what about the writing helped you reach your decision.

> Everybody watched—but nearly everybody was disappointed.
> That, in a nutshell, seems to be the general reaction to Monday night's CBS grand finale of "MASH," which attracted an enormous audience and unwittingly demonstrated just how badly the program had degenerated during the last four seasons.
> An estimated 125 million viewers, many of them longtime "MASH" diehards, were subjected to a terribly limp, slow-moving 2½ hours that culminated with the end of the Korean War and the homeward movement of the leading characters. It was mediocre television, a tribute to the monumental greed of CBS and 20th Century-Fox, both of whom have no apparent concern for preserving the dignity of a series that once was the very best TV had to offer. (Gary Deeb, "Finale a MisMASH of Poor Acting, Bad Drama," *Lafayette* [Indiana] *Journal and Courier.* March 4, 1983)

Is the writer's main purpose informative or affective?

_____

_____

Pioneer 10, which left Earth 11 years ago, is about to become the first spacecraft to leave the known solar system. On June 13, as of 8 a.m. Eastern time, it will be farther from the sun than Neptune, which, because of Pluto's elliptical orbit, is now the outermost planet. *Pioneer 10* will be 2,823,685,909 miles from the sun and hurtling at 30,558 miles per hour into the void.

It has been a hardy traveler. Launched in 1972, the nuclear-powered spacecraft was designed to operate 21 months, long enough to pay the first visit to Jupiter. Today, after a trip through searing Jovian radiation and the asteroid belt, every instrument except the magneometer still works. The eight-watt transmitter has sent nearly 126 billion bits of information, which now take more than four hours to reach giant receivers on Earth. Its radio signals should be audible for seven more years. NASA scientists will be tracking them to detect any tug on the craft from a tenth planet or an invisible star that might lie out there. They'll also be studying the boundary where the sun's electromagnetic influence ends and interstellar space begins. ("Starward Ho! *Pioneer* Exits the Solar System," *Science 83*)

Is the writer's main purpose informative or affective?

You may recall that article published several weeks ago in *The Washington Post* revealing a new category of misery . . . computer widows. Computer widows are apparently the latest casualty of the miracle machine that has been hailed as both a world savior and a world nemesis.

The article described life . . . or rather the lack of it . . . with computer addicts who spend every evening and weekend squirreled away in a room with their home computers—playing games, inventing games, writing programs, and looking for yet another innovative application.

The article went on to document how the personal computer has become a source of serious family distress. The computer addicts neglect their wives, ignore their children, and scorn their household responsibilities.

The home computer was blamed for disrupting normal relationships between man and wife, and the story reported several instances where an Apple (the computer Apple) a day was cited as a cause of divorce. (Benjamin H. Alexander, "Impact of Computers on Human Behavior: The Future Is Not Now." *Vital Speeches*)

Is the writer's main purpose informative or affective?

_____

_____

_____

_____

Mercury moves with great speed in its journey about the sun, averaging about 30 miles a second to complete its circuit in 88 of our days. Mercury rotates upon its axis over a period of nearly 59 days, thus exposing all of its surface periodically to the sun. It is believed that the surface passing before the sun may have a temperature of about 800 degrees F., while the temperature on the side turned temporarily away from the sun does not fall as low as might be expected. This night temperature has been described by Russian astronomers as "room temperature"—possibly about 70 degrees. This would contradict the former belief that Mercury did not possess an atmosphere, for some sort of atmosphere would be needed to retain the fierce solar radiation that strikes Mercury. (*The World Almanac and Book of Facts 1983*)

Is the writer's main purpose informative or affective?

_____

_____

_____

_____

Exercise 2

Read these excerpts from advertising copy and determine which parts are informative and which are affective. In the space provided, write three or four informative words or phrases from the ad and three or four affective words or phrases.

ADVERTISEMENT FOR PERRIER WATER

Still clear, pure and sparkling, and minus all those additives that civilization has invented. There's no sugar. No artificial sweetner. No calories. There's no caffeine, no coloring. And Perrier is recommended for salt-free diets, as well.

In modern times, when most beverages are made with water that's been disinfected, softened, oxidated or chlorinated, it's nice also to know that Perrier is naturally filtered as it rises to the surface from its deep underground source.

And so our only concession to civilization is the green Perrier bottle. Because without it, you would never get to enjoy Perrier.

Perrier. Earth's first doft drink. Not manufactured, but created by the earth when it was new.

Informative words and phrases: _____

_____

_____

_____

Affective words and phrases: _____

_____

_____

ADVERTISEMENT FOR BMW AUTOMOBILES

The 320i was inspired not by any sudden trendy sedan but by a heritage spanning 6 decades.

A heritage that's resulted in 31 world and European racing titles and performance cars like the 320i.

Which is why the 320i's fuel-injected engine is so responsive up through the gears, yet still able to run all day at cruising speeds if asked.

Its fully independent suspension explains why BMW owners seek out winding roads. Where its steering provides the delightful sensation of precisely guiding, rather than aiming, the car through its paces.

And its mileage figures, in a car with such performance credentials, read like misprints: an EPA-estimated 25mpg, 36 mpg highway.

Informative words and phrases: _____

_____

_____

_____

Affective words and phrases: _____

_____

_____

ADVERTISEMENT FOR THE MARLBOROUGH HOTEL

Back Bay Boston's most prestigious address. A reservoir of turn-of-the-century charm for the discerning traveler. Experience the amenities of a more polished age: canopied beds, upholstered window seats, walnut paneling, gleaming brass. Just minutes from the sophisticated shopping districts of Newbury Street and Copley Place. The Marlborough: a grand hotel in a grand city. For reservations call your travel agent or (617) 936-1000.

Informative words and phrases: _____

_____

_____

Affective words and phrases: _____

_____

_____

Exercise 3

In the following two excerpts the writers offer personal experience and use subjective and objective words. Underline as many examples of subjective words, which convey the writer's personal reactions, as you can find and decide whether the writing is primarily subjective or objective.

> To return to the old country after a longish absence is to find oneself feeling like a nervous guest in some reactionary Lilliput. In one of his more extreme moments, Evelyn Waugh described his experience of Labor government in Britain as "living under foreign occupation." I think I know the effect he was striving to convey. As I arrived, Margaret Thatcher had just called for a return to "Victorian values"; the British Navy had announced that it would intercept a boatload of Argentine war widows if they came anywhere near the Falkland Islands; and our senior Tory historian had just fallen for a palpable hoax designed to sweeten the memory of the Third Reich. Welcome home, I thought savagely as I paid for the taxi with a fistful of the new L1 coins, which serve to remind us that the national currency is Lilliputian too. The next morning, *The Times* of London gave prominent and respectful coverage to a bovine speech from the Queen's husband, His Grace the Duke of Edinburgh, to the effect that nuclear weapons are an indispensable deterrent. (Christopher Hitchen, "Minority Report," *The Nation*)

Is this writing primarily subjective or objective? Why?_____

_____

_____

_____

_____

I was raised in New Jersey, a dense and very particular place to the sturdy Irish Catholic peasant clan I come from, but an unplace, at best a place between places, to me. First Elizabeth, a decaying industrial port city; then, when I was on the edge of adolescence, my family joined the great postwar migration to Beaver Cleaver country, buying a large, four-apartment investment of a home in the only tacky neighborhood of a suburb fifteen or so miles inland. As far as our relatives in Elizabeth were concerned, it might as well have been Utah. We quit seeing them except on ceremonial occasions, which became fewer in number each year. We also quit going to church every Sunday. My father had to work and my mother couldn't drive. There went the faith of generations. (Gene Lyon, "Why I Live Where I Live," *Esquire*)

Is this writing primarily subjective or objective? Why? _____

_____

_____

_____

_____

Exercise 4

Choose one of the following topics and write about a personal experience suggested by the topic. Write both a subjective account, which conveys your personal reactions, and an objective, factual, impersonal version of the same experience. Afterwards, share your writing with a small group of other writers. Ask them if you have maintained a consistent tone in both pieces of writing.

Suggested topics:
    a stay in the hospital
    an unusual vacation
    being lost
    entering a contest
    learning to ride a bike or drive a car
    starting school
    being on your own for the first time
    your first major purchase
    a special birthday
    a close call

Topic: _____

Subjective version: _____

_____

_____

_____

_____

_____

_____

_____

Objective version: _____

_____

_____

_____

_____

_____

_____

_____

_____

Suggestions for revision from other readers: _____

_____

_____

_____

_____

_____

_____

_____

_____

Distance

Exercise 1

Is the tone of the following excerpts personal or impersonal? Look at the
word choices, kinds of comments, and sentence structure to decide. In
your response, explain how you arrived at your decision and give examples
from the selection that support your evaluation.

> Like any properly brought up Southern girl, I used to spend a lot of
> time in graveyards. On summer afternoons we'd pile into my mother's
> green Chevrolet—my Aunt Vera, her daughter June (four years my senior),
> and often also a massive, aged female relation. Somehow we'd fit ourselves
> into the front and back seats, the women in print dresses and hairnets and
> no stockings, we two kids in shorts, and Mother would gun on down the
> road at 40mph with every window open.
>
> The boredom, for my cousin June and me, was a heavy as passion. Our
> mothers never packed a picnic basket, or even a thermos of lemonade or
> any refreshments beyond a package of chewing gum, which they meted out
> late in the day, half a stick at a time, June was not only older than I but

smarter, and we'd soon be brawling. She knew the drill: she'd tease me about my freckles or who I "liked" ("It's that little drip Charles Lynas, ain't it?"), and like some perplexed, furious puppy, I'd attack. Since my aggression made the most racket, I got the punishment. (Shirley Abbott, "Southern Women," *Harper's*)

Your response: _____

_____

_____

_____

All my early life lies open to my eye within five city blocks. When I passed the school, I went sick with all my old fear of it. With its standard New York public-school brown brick courtyard shut in on three sides of the square and the pretentious battelments overlooking that cockpit in which I can still smell the fiery sheen of the rubber ball, it looks like a factory over which has been imposed the facade of a castle. It gave me the shivers to stand up in that courtyard again; I felt as if I had been mustered back into the service of those Friday morning "tests" that were the terror of my childhood.

It was never learning I associated with that school: only the necessity to succeed, to get ahead of the others in the daily struggle to "make a good impression" on our teachers, who grimly, earily, and often with ill-concealed distaste watched against our relapsing into the natural savagery they expected of Brownsville boys. The white, cool, thinly ruled record book sat over us from their desks all day long, and had remorselessly entered into it each day—in blue ink if we had passed, in red ink if we had not—our attendance, our conduct, our "effort," our merits and demerits; and to the last possible decimal point in calculation, our standing in an unending series of "tests"—surprise tests, daily tests, weekly tests, formal midterm tests, final tests. They never stopped trying to dig out of us whatever small morsel of fact we had managed to get down the night before. (Alfred Kazin, *A Walker in the City*)

Your response: _____

_____

_____

American families differ greatly in their expectations about what going to college will mean in their children's lives. In the intellectual community to which my parents belonged, college was as necessary as learning to read. It was an intellectual experience and the gateway to the rest of my life. All my life I expected to go to college and I was prepared to enjoy it.

My mother had included drawing lessons in the advantages she had wrestled for me out of the various strange environments in which we lived, and I had enough talent to be encouraged to become a painter. However, when I was told by my artist cousins that in order to become a painter I should go to art school and skip college, I gave up the idea. For me, not to go to college was, in a sense, not to become a full human being. (Margaret Mead, *Blackberry Winter*)

Your response: _____

_____

_____

_____

I get the willies when I see closed doors. Even at work, where I am doing so well now, the sight of a closed door is sometimes enough to make me dread that something horrible is happening behind it, something that is going to affect me adversely; if I am tired and dejected from a night of lies or booze or sex or just plain nerves and insomnia, I can almost smell the disaster mounting invisibly and flooding out toward me through the frosted glass panes. My hands may perspire, and my voice may come out strange. I wonder why.

Something must have happened to me sometime. (Joseph Heller, *Something Happened*)

Your response: _____

_____

_____

_____

_____

Exercise 2

Reread the excerpts above to determine the degree to which each selection is close and personal or remote and impersonal. Categorize each selection and write the author's name in the appropriate place along the scale provided below. If possible, work with a small group of other writers to arrive at your decision.

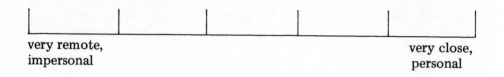

very remote,   very close,
impersonal   personal

Exercise 3

Think of a topic for which you could write both a personal, close response and also an impersonal, remote version of the same topic. For example, consider the following suggestions:

1. Your dorm room is so cramped, cold, and noisy that you want to ask for a change of room assignment. Write a personal version of the problem in a letter to a close relative, such as a parent or guardian who must agree to the change. Write a more impersonal version to the dorm administrator who needs to know the specifics of your problem in order to make a decision.
2. Now that you have been enrolled in college for a while, you have some suggestions for how high school students should prepare for college. Send a relatively impersonal version of your suggestions to your old high school newspaper, which will publish the column. Write another, more personal version to a favorite cousin of yours who is now a high school junior and is wondering how she can best get ready for college. Offer her the same suggestions included in your newspaper column.
3. Pick an area in which you have some knowledge or expertise, such as tennis, skiing, computer programming, counseling, cooking, working with the elderly, or farming. Write a short "how to" paper that offers some basic instructions or an introduction to this topic. First, write a somewhat impersonal version that could be used in a magazine article or book of instructions for the general reader. Then write a more personal version for a friend or yours who has written to ask for your help on the subject. Include the same information in both versions.

Topic: _____

Impersonal version: _____

_____

_____

_____

_____

_____

_____

_____

Personal version: _____

_____

_____

_____

_____

_____

_____

_____

_____

STYLE

Exercise 1

To decide whether the style of the following selections is formal, moderate, or colloquial, analyze each of the selections by answering the questions that follow.

> If you want to buy a small computer, there are three types of vendors worth considering: the computer store, the systems house, and the office equipment supplier.
>
> You can go to a computer store, which, as its name would imply, stocks and sells computers, just as a stereo store stocks and sells stereo systems.
>
> You can go to a *systems house*, which is usually a small group of consultants who are in the business of packaging programs with microcomputers in order to generate complete, working small business systems. Many computer stores also operate as systems houses.
>
> Office equipment suppliers are now beginning to carry small computers. These are the guys who in the past you counted on for typewriters, small copy machines, business calculators, and the like. Many small office computers are now sufficiently inexpensive and easy enough to use for typical office equipment suppliers to handle them.
>
> Office equipment suppliers will probably become an increasingly important factor in the small business computer market during the next few years. (Adam Osborne and Steven Cook, *Business System Buyer' Guide*)

1. Sentence Structure

   How many sentences are there? _____

   How many of these sentences are fragments? _____

   What is the average number of words per sentence? _____

   How many words are there in the longest sentence? _____
   What kinds of sentence patterns (standard, balanced, and periodic) are used and how frequently does each appear?

   _____

   _____

   _____

2. Diction

   What percentage of the words contain more than two syllables? _____

   How many contractions are used? _____

   If there are learned words, list some: _____

   _____

   _____

3. Tone

   Is the writer's attitude primarily informative or affective? _____

   _____

   Is the distance between the author and reader slight or great? _____

   _____

4. Your summary:

   _____

   _____

   _____

   _____

   _____

   In the 20th century, it has become disappointingly clear that many people find totalitarian societies attractive. It is one of the terrifying ironies of
our time that some of our most gifted people persist in finding such societies attractive in exact proportion to their physical distance from life in
those societies. Millions of others value living in a democratic system; millions have willingly died defending freedom, opposing the millions who
have sought to destroy it. This latter fact is for me the meaning of James
Joyce's bitter jape that "history is a nightmare from which I am trying to
awake."

   Joyce died in the year of Pearl Harbor, before the incomprehensible in-
justice and brutality of Nazi concentration camps and Soviet gulags were
widely known. Before Pol Pot's murder of more than one-third of his fellow

Cambodians. Before Poalnd's Kremlin-sponsored imprisoning of an entire population which dared to demand a voice in the disposition of their labor. Joyce's history is a thriving cancer and his nightmare infinitely more terrifying than even he imagined. (Leo Cherne, "Striving for a Just Society," *Vital Speeches*)

1. Sentence Structure

   How many sentences are there? _____

   How many of these sentences are fragments? _____

   What is the average number of words per sentence? _____

   How many words are there in the longest sentence? _____
   What kinds of sentence patterns (standard, balanced, and periodic) are used and how frequently does each appear?

   _____

   _____

   _____

2. Diction

   What percentage of the words contain more than two syllables? _____

   How many contractions are used? _____

   If there are learned words, list some: _____

   _____

   _____

3. Tone

   Is the writer's attitude primarily informative or affective? _____

   _____

   Is the distance between the author and reader slight or great? _____

   _____

4. Your summary:

_____

_____

_____

_____

_____

When a knuckleball leaves the pitcher's hand, it is not unlike the game of baseball itself: slow, static, and delivered with deft precision. But also like the game, the results of the delivery are quite the opposite: The ball's flight to the plate is unpredictable, quick to change, and dramatic when it does. And it is a joy to watch—if you don't have a bat in your hand. . . .

Most knuckleball pitchers hold the ball with the fingertips, not the knuckles, and throw it while keeping the wrist stiff. The pitch travels about 50 miles per hour, slower than curves and fastballs. But what it lacks in speed it makes up in movement. It darts and weaves, dips and sails, with the seeming capriciousness of George Steinbrunner contemplating his team's managerial post. The ball is so erratic, catchers working with knuckleballers use an oversized glove. Even then they have problems. "The best way to catch a knuckleball," according to former catcher Bob Uecker, "is to wait until the ball stops rolling and then pick it up." (William F. Allman, "Twisting Slowly in the Wind," *Science 83*)

1. Sentence Structure

   How many sentences are there? _____

   How many of these sentences are fragments? _____

   What is the average number of words per sentence? _____

   How many words are there in the longest sentence? _____
   What kinds of sentence patterns (standard, balanced, and periodic) are used and how frequently does each appear?

   _____

   _____

   _____

2. Diction

   What percentage of the words contain more than two syllables? _____

   How many contractions are used? _____

   If there are learned words, list some: _____

   _____

   _____

3. Tone

   Is the writer's attitude primarily informative or affective? _____

   _____

   Is the distance between the author and reader slight or great? _____

   _____

4. Your summary:

   _____

   _____

   _____

   _____

   _____

   The root problems of American education can be found in "A Nation at Risk," the report of the National Commission on Excellence in Education, but they are not the ones named by the commissioners. Those seventeen august educators, plus a token parent, toiling under a $785,000 grant and a mandate from the Department of Education, zeroed in on the length of the school day, the average load of homework, and the teaching of the "new basics" (computer science, for example) as subjects for remedial action. No doubt there is room for improvement in such areas. But as they appear on the national report card, they sound more like effects than causes of the "tide of mediocrity" the commissioners see engulfing the country. And what is wrong with education turns out to be less a matter of school administrators than of social and political direction. . . .

The fiercest competitor, of course, is the Soviet Union; American students are found to score lower on most achievement tests than they did "26 years ago when Sputnik was launched." What with the proliferation of frilly subjects such as cooking, American students are in danger of losing the high-tech race to their Russian counterprats. ("Arming Education," *The Nation*)

1. Sentence Structure

   How many sentences are there? _____

   How many of these sentences are fragments? _____

   What is the average number of words per sentence? _____

   How many words are there in the longest sentence? _____
   What kinds of sentence patterns (standard, balanced, and periodic) are used and how frequently does each appear?

   _____

   _____

   _____

2. Diction

   What percentage of the words contain more than two syllables? _____

   How many contractions are used? _____

   If there are learned words, list some: _____

   _____

   _____

3. Tone

   Is the writer's attitude primarily informative or affective? _____

   _____

   Is the distance between the author and reader slight or great? _____

   _____

4. Your summary:

_____

_____

_____

_____

_____

     Astronomy is not the oldest profession, but it is the oldest science. From 1500 B.C. in Babylon, and perhaps before, people recorded the motions of heavenly bodies for tracking the seasons, planting crops, and navigating. And as in other healthy sciences, the earliest questions ranged beyond practical applications. Outdoors, on a crystal night, celestial mysteries spill over the limits of practicality. Among the ancient riddles were the little misty patches, or nebulae, noted by the Greek astronomers Hipparchus and Ptolemy—too distant for atmospheric clouds and too diffuse for single stars. What were they?

    In 1610, with his new gadget the telescope, Galileo was delighted to find that "the stars [misty patches] which have been called by every one of the astronomers up to this day, nebulous, are groups of small stars set thick together in a wonderful way, although each one of them . . . escapes our sight." Galileo had discovered star clusters, each consisting of many stars orbiting each other under their mutual gravity and created, we think, by the proximity of stars during their formations. Today, despite superior telescopes, high-speed computers, and dogged theoretical calculations, we remain baffled by the workings of star clusters. (Alan Lightman, "Misty Patches in the Sky," *Science 83*)

1. Sentence Structure

How many sentences are there? _____

How many of these sentences are fragments? _____

What is the average number of words per sentence? _____

How many words are there in the longest sentence? _____
What kinds of sentence patterns (standard, balanced, and periodic) are used and how frequently does each appear?

_____

_____

_____

2. Diction

   What percentage of the words contain more than two syllables? _____

   How many contractions are used? _____

   If there are learned words, list some: _____

   _____

   _____

3. Tone

   Is the writer's attitude primarily informative or affective? _____

   _____

   Is the distance between the author and reader slight or great? _____

   _____

4. Your summary:

   _____

   _____

   _____

   _____

   _____

   _____

   _____

   _____

   _____

Exercise 2

The students who wrote the three essays from which the following excerpts are taken could profit from some reader evaluation of their style. Read the excerpts and offer some comments that will help the writers achieve a consistent, effective style that is appropriate for their purposes.

> As a child, like most other children, I had a secret place which was mine alone. As far as I knew, no one else ever knew about it. When the stress of trying to deal with the complexities of the adult world became too much to handle, I would go to the clearing in the woods behind my house to just sit and phase out. To me it was, and still is, a beautiful place.
>
> One of the contributing factors of its beauty was the totally natural scenery. This small mead was completely encircled by trees of a great variety. Alone, the trees added a beauty of their own in the fall when the leaves changed colors from green to blushing shades of red and orange. The trees also added to the beauty of the clearing by letting tiny shafts of light occasionally filter through their gently rustling leaves to dance across the moss-covered ground in an undulating pattern. Scattered around on the ground were decaying logs silently paying tribute to what were once great trees. One of these logs lay across the small stream that divided the clearing, forming a natural bridge that you could use with perfect safety even if you're the nervous type like me. This was my place, my space. You probably won't believe it, but this natural beauty has radiated itself into my mind and is a habitat to be cherished. (Student writer)

Your comments and suggestions: _____

_____

_____

_____

_____

_____

> It is 10:30 p.m. on a Sunday night. There are six of us up in our sixth floor suite munching down on our third batch of salty, buttery popcorn. What is the one thing we need to go with our mouthwatering popcorn? Tab! However, the only place Tab is sold is located on the main floor of our dorm in the vending machines, and we have on our pajamas and robes. Now one may say that we should not be modest and that we should just

© 1984 Houghton Mifflin Company

make a quick dash downstairs, get our Tabs, and run right back up to the suite. Well, that would be fine with us; in fact, we don't care who sees us in our robes. However, it is against dormitory rules to be downstairs with robes or pajamas on.

Well, our thirst just won't quit, so we decide to venture downstairs with our pajamas and robes still on and cop ourselves some Tab. Just as I am about to put my thirty-five cents into the machine, I hear a loud, "Hold it right there!" Oh no, we have been caught by the feared dormitory director. She informs us of our rights and sentences us to appear before the dorm judiciary board. We plead our poor case in front of the board, and we are then let off the hook with a warning not to do it again.

The question I must raise in this issue is this: Is there any logical reason for this unnecessary rule? The obvious answer is no. In today's society, there is no reason why women residing in the all-woman residence halls cannot be seen in their own living units with bathrobes on. (Student writer)

Your comments and suggestions: _____

_____

_____

_____

_____

It's like the words to the song, "over the river and through the woods, to grandmother's house we go," except instead of going to grandmother's house I'm going to my favorite piece of land. The river isn't a river either, but a little creek that almost completely surrounds the acreage. Actually, to get there, I have to tramp through the pines, where the wind howls and the trees moan, jump over the creek, scramble up a slippery hill, and dodge the sticker bushes. Yet it is well worth all this spent energy to be able to explore the little meadow at the top.

That meadow is the piece of land that I hope to buy some day. I stumbled upon it while exploring the woods around my parents' house several years ago. Since then, I have made numerous attempts to find it again, but it wasn't until last summer that I was able to do so. Oh, the joy of once more seeing that quiet place. (Student writer)

Your comments and suggestions: _____

_____

_____

_____

_____

_____

Recently a member of the English department of San Jose State University held a Bulwer-Lytton Fiction Contest. He invited contestants to imagine the worst novel conceivable and then to write its first sentence. The winning entry was:

> The camel died quite suddenly on the second day and Selina fretted sulkily and, buffing her already impeccable nails—not for the first time since the journey began—pondered snidely if this would dissolve into a vignette of minor inconveniences like all the other holidays spent with Basil. (Reported in an AP story included in the *Lafayette* [Indiana] *Journal and Courier,* May 8, 1983)

Since writing bad prose can be instructive, try a similar exercise, which can help you learn more about style by seeing what happens when some important guidelines are not followed. Listed below is some practical advice about style that you generally want to follow. Ignore it, however.

1. Let your purpose be your guide.
2. Generally, choose a moderate style.
3. Keep your style consistent.
4. Try to see your writing as your reader will see it.
5. Be as specific as you can.
6. Revise for style.

Instead of following these guidelines, write a paragraph that deliberately ignores as much of that practical advice as possible. Work in a small group with several other writers to create the best possible example that you can of bad style.

_____

_____

_____

10
Persuasion

CHANGING THE READER'S IMAGE

Exercise 1

To see how often persuasion is used around you and on you, watch for instances of persuasion at work. Consider the TV programs you watch; the newspapers, magazines, and signs you see around you; the advertisements you notice; the comments of friends, teachers, and others; and the mail you receive. Take notes on the kinds of persuasion you find, and in the space below list at least five instances of persuasion that you've recently encountered. In a sentence or two for each instance, describe where you encountered the example, how it was delivered (TV ad, store sign, or the like), and the belief, opinion, or action that the message conveyed. To what degree were you persuaded to agree?

1. _____

   _____

2. _____

   _____

3. _____

   _____

4. _____

   _____

5. _____

_____

Exercise 2

Much of what people believe can be divided into shallow beliefs and deeply rooted beliefs. Shallow beliefs can be altered in the face of adequate proof and changed without drastic effect. For example, someone might believe that a particular kind of music is dull, boring, and not worth the time to listen to, but the person may change that belief after attending a thoroughly enjoyable concert featuring that particular type of music. Deeply rooted beliefs, however, cannot be given up as easily or without causing a major or crucial change in a person's life.

A. List five beliefs that you could change without drastically affecting your life.

1. _____

_____

2. _____

_____

3. _____

_____

4. _____

_____

5. _____

_____

B. List five beliefs that are firmly rooted in your mind.

1. _____

_____

2. _____

_____

3. _____

_____

4. _____

_____

5. _____

_____

Exercise 3

Interview another person in order to find three shallow and three deeply
rooted beliefs held by that person.

Person interviewed: _____

A. Three shallow beliefs

1. _____

_____

2. _____

_____

3. _____

_____

B. Three deeply rooted beliefs

1. _____

_____

2. _____

_____

3. _____

_____

Exercise 4

Which of these beliefs would you characterize as shallower and which as more deeply rooted in your mind. Choose the alternative that is closest to your own beliefs and then rate it by putting a check at the appropriate place on the scale.

A. Women today generally are (are not) treated fairly.

1	2	3	4	5
very shallow				very deep

B. Religion is (is not) an important part of my life.

1	2	3	4	5
very shallow				very deep

C. The most popular TV shows are (are not) the afternoon game shows.

1	2	3	4	5
very shallow				very deep

D. Cities are (are not) unwholesome places in which to bring up children.

1	2	3	4	5
very shallow				very deep

E. Freedom of speech should (should not) be limited if it endangers national security.

1	2	3	4	5
very shallow				very deep

F. Drinking moderate amounts of alcohol every day does (does not) in-
jure a person's health.

1	2	3	4	5
very shallow				very deep

G. Having an important, high-paying, high-status job is (is not) an important element in happiness.

1	2	3	4	5
very shallow				very deep

H. Drunk drivers are (are not) the major cause of highway deaths.

1	2	3	4	5
very shallow				very deep

I. Preserving the natural environment for future generations is (is not)
crucially important.

1	2	3	4	5
very shallow				very deep

J. Being able to speak and write well is (is not) important to success in
most careers.

1	2	3	4	5
very shallow				very deep

K. Sunbathing is (is not) an unhealthy activity with potentially dangerous
side effects.

1	2	3	4	5
very shallow				very deep

L. Wearing a heavy coat in winter is (is not) warmer than wearing three
layers of lighter clothing.

1	2	3	4	5
very shallow				very deep

Exercise 5

To be persuasive writers must learn to know their readers' beliefs. Using
the list above, interview another person to find out how that person would
rate these beliefs on the scale you used for your own rating. Ask the person to choose the alternative closest to his or her general system of beliefs.
What did you learn about that person's beliefs? Summarize your answers
here, noting which beliefs are deeply held by that person and which could
be changed by presenting the person with convincing reasons. Compare
that person's responses with your own.

_____

_____

_____

_____

_____

_____

_____

FITTING THE PERSUASION TO THE AUDIENCE

Exercise 1

One way to identify an audience's attitudes and beliefs is to ask them.
Choose a topic and a local audience for which you think you can predict
the responses. (The suggested list of topics below may be helpful.) Write
down the topic you choose, the type of audience you will interview, and
the responses you predict you'll get. Then, interview a representative sample of this audience by asking them where they stand on the topic and
what issues they are most concerned with. For example, for an audience
composed of students at your college who use the library, you might pick
a topic such as the adequacy of the study facilities in the library. Predict

the answers you expect to get when you question some students studying in the library and then interview the students to see how close you came to their actual answers.

Suggested topics:

The nicest or most attractive feature of the area is _____

The worst season of the year in this area is _____

The major economic problem of the state is _____
Instituting prayer in the public schools is unconstitutional.
Counseling services at this college are adequate.
The primary importance of a college education is that it prepares people for careers.
Alcohol is a greater problem among college students than drugs.
Minorities in this community are treated fairly.

Topic: _____

_____

Audience: _____

Your prediction of this audience's response: _____

_____

_____

_____

Your summary of their responses: _____

_____

_____

_____

How well did your hypothesis match what you found? _____

_____

_____

_____

Exercise 2

What are some beliefs that advertisements assume will be accepted by their audiences? For example, a toothpaste ad that shows someone getting a date after whitening his or her teeth assumes that audiences believe that the color of a person's teeth is very important to social success. What other beliefs are assumed in ads you see? List three of these beliefs and, if possible, clip examples of the ads to the page.

1. _____

   _____

   _____

2. _____

   _____

   _____

3. _____

   _____

   _____

(Clip ads here)

MEANS OF PERSUASION

Trustworthiness

Exercise 1

In order to persuade, a writer must win the reader's trust by being knowledgeable and fair. How trustworthy are the writers of the following excerpts? If possible, form a small group to decide the degree to which each of these writers appears to be well informed and fair.

> The prejudice Northerners feel towards Southerners is roughly parallel to that felt by English people towards Americans, and is compounded of many of the same ingredients—a thoroughgoing dislike of their public policies, contempt for their level of education and culture, and a sort of instinctive recoil at the sound of the accent—larded in both cases, it must be said, with a thick layer of that particular form of snobbishness that sneers at the provincial. It is distasteful to the Northerner that a human being should have the given name of Lady Bird; it grates on the Northern ear to hear an educated person say "sumpn" and "prolly," or speak of a "mess of fried chicken" pronounced "maiss of frad chickn."
>
> The photographs that appear so regularly in the newspapers of white faces caught in the act of hate outside some school or drugstore fill the Northerner with uneasiness and almost incredulity; for when the Northerner segregates and discriminates, he does it on the whole slyly rather than overtly, and without passion.
>
> Thus the white South comes to be pictured in the Northern mind as an undifferentiated, arid wasteland of the human intellect and spirit, a hopeless mess of a place, cluttered with irrationality and ignorance, incongruously smeared over with a sticky coating of sugary politeness and sentimentality.
>
> All the same, there are hints that changes may be on the way: a high-school student's appeal for reason in Little Rock; a white minister leading his child past hostile mobs to school in New Orleans; white college kids extending the hand of friendship to three black classmates at Georgia Tech.
>
> (Jessica Mitford, *Poison Penmanship: The Gentle Art of Muckraking*)

How trustworthy is this writer? _____

_____

_____

_____

_____

_____

_____

_____

TWIST AND SHOUT

Pity the First Amendment. How many of its beneficiaries bludgeon it! The President, too. He twists it in a sermon about sin and social policy, and in a national security directive about the official clearance of information. But the Jeffersonians in the land cannot complain that violence to this primary American value comes only from above. Unfortunately, it comes also from below. A new method for the prevention of free discussion has been introduced into American political culture. It is the heckler's veto; or, as *The Nation* philosophically put it, "the right to heckle." It was tested with great success upon U.N. Ambassador Jeane Kirkpatrick, who was driven from a platform at Berkeley on February 15 by supporters of democracy in Central America, and was disinvited to speak at commencement at Smith College because the campus administration callously refused to protect her against demonstrators. There have been other victims of the heckler's veto as well. When Sheik Yamani came to Kansas City to give his excuses for his audience's heating bills, he was shouted down, and continued his lecture after the police removed the shouters. (They were Iranians, who did not inherit a First Amendment.) And, at Stanford Law School, Jack Greenberg of the N.A.A.C.P., who has won more civil rights cases than any other man, did not even make it to the lectern; black student protesters saw to it that his course was closed down.

The issue is not merely civility, though we will be forgiven for the bourgeois belief that it matters, too. The issue is the theory of an open society. The heckler's veto is a challenge to the proudly procedural character of democracy. A democracy is premised not upon the content of your belief, but upon your right to it. Indeed, it is the indifference of our system of public discussion to the content of what is discussed that makes the system free. Anything goes, says our sublime amendment. Not the heckler. Anything correct goes, says he, and he will be happy to tell you what correctness is. With the introduction of a criterion of correctness, of philosophical and political preconditions for participation in the public discussion, the theory of an open society is tampered with.

Heckling may not look like a moral or political offense, but it is. It is an expression of a desire to silence the other. It is, in short, a petty form of repression; and it is one of the many luxuries of American public life that we may cry havoc even about repression's petty forms. A large number of organizations representing college administrators, teachers, and students have done just that. They came together to issue a statement that declares: "The 'hiss and boo,' when they go beyond brief expressions of opposition and become instruments to silence those with whom one disagrees, are inappropriate at any public gathering, but especially in places of higher learning."

Meanwhile at Berkeley it feels like old times. *The Nation*'s correspondent (Mario Savio, phone home) discusses "the competing claims of hecklers and lecturers"—no doubt another of the many contradictions of monopoly capitalism. "The First Amendment," he writes, "was designed to empower ordinary citizens against officialdom." This man should go back and hit the books. The First Amendment proscribes "abridging the freedom of speech," and abridged is exactly what Mrs. Kirkpatrick's freedom was. It goes on to speak of "the right of the people . . . to petition the government for a redress of grievances," but it is not clear what the hecklers' grievances are, except that there exist views different from their own. Mrs. Kirkpatrick's views on El Salvador, however, are irrelevant to her right to make them known.

No. Do not pity the First Amendment. Pity those who do not understand it. (unsigned editorial in *The New Republic*, April 25, 1983)

How trustworthy is this writer? _____

_____

_____

_____

_____

_____

_____

_____

_____

Exercise 2

Find a movie review that critiques a movie you have seen. How trustworthy is the writer of the review? Clip a copy of the review here and then write a short evaluation of the author's trustworthiness. If you can, try to locate an advertisement for the movie that quotes critics. Do these quotations generally agree with the judgment of the reviewer you read?

_____

_____

_____

_____

_____

_____

_____

_____

_____

_____

Emotional Appeals

Exercise 1

Emotional appeals that persuade readers most effectively dramatize through examples in order to personalize the problem. How effective are the emotional appeals in the following excerpts?

Philadelphia, Pennsylvania: Ridge Avenue, William Penn High, Reynolds Funeral Parlor (where I last saw Mamma), the fish market, the Pearl Theatre, Central High. Yes, I, too, know Philadelphia. Where did it all go? Where did we let it all go? Another city heading toward decay—sure, there are still beautiful parts—yet the spoils are so general, rottenness is so evident.

Do cities cry? How many times I've waited for trains at North Philadelphia station. Now it's so frightening, you dare not stop. Columbia Avenue, land lying still, people frightened to look left or right as they walk—if they walk. Can a town of decent people reach out and save itself? Can the Liberty Bell be rung again? The mayor, governors, justice department, president, and ourselves search. What's so wrong with other countries that's not so wrong with ourselves?

It's time we made our lives once again our own. Do we waste away our lives to the pace of problems: race problems, school problems, political problems—protest here, strike there—school out, bus in, bus out—the prisons full, the criminals free. The system works, they say. In Philadelphia the Constitution was signed. In the daylight. In the morning. By free men, freely. Wouldn't it be wonderful to walk down the streets of this great old town without looking over your shoulder? Ring that bell, Liberty. (Pearl Bailey, in *Hurry Up, American, & Spit*)

How effective is this writer's use of emotional appeals? Prove your answer by citing examples from the essay.

_____

_____

_____

_____

_____

_____

_____

_____

_____

_____

Who's afraid of Louisa M. Alcott? Well, Louisa M. Alcott, for one; and, for another, me.

I'm afraid of her in a quite straightforward way—because she makes me cry. Being myself an almost wholly unsentimental writer, I'm not a bit afraid of her example, which doesn't tempt me. It's not as a writer but as a reader that I fear her. . . .

I was driven back to Louisa M. Alcott, whom I hadn't read since I was fourteen, by the recent revival on television of the old film of *Little Women*. By the old film I mean the one with the young Katharine Hepburn—and there I instantly caution myself not to render unto Alcott credit which belongs to Hepburn. The cinematic personality of Katharine Hepburn (for which I imagine the credit belongs to the real-life personality of Katharine Hepburn) is one of those purely poetic literary inventions like Rosalind or the very idea of a seraph. Tears shed over Hepburn are diamonds, cutting clean and deep lacerations into the cheeks they course down. They have no connexion at all with the synthetically pearled snail-track left by the tears of sentimentality. It was just Louisa M. Alcott's good posthumous luck that Hepburn played Jo and that the high ruffled necks of 'period' clothes (to use the word in its purely evocative or estate agent's sense) set off to perfection the essentially tragic sineviness of the Hepburn throat. (Brigid Brophy, *Don't Never Forget*)

How effective is this writer's use of emotional appeals? Prove your answer by citing examples from the excerpt.

Exercise 2

Look in newspapers, magazines, and letters to find advertisements that seek charitable contributions. Find two examples and clip copies of them here. To what degree are the emotional appeals effective? How do the requests appeal to your emotions?

_____

_____

_____

_____

_____

_____

  Think of a general problem that exists in the world around you—malnourished children in India, the disappearance of unspoiled wilderness, or modern society's neglect of old people, for example. Or consider a problem closer to your immediate surroundings—landlords who do not adequately maintain rental apartments, lack of space for student parking, street crime, or perhaps drug abuse. Then, in order to practice using emotional appeals to persuade, think of a way to personalize the problem for an article in a local newspaper.

  Begin by defining the problem, and then go on to consider how you would personalize it. Write out a plan for accomplishing what you intend to do. For example, would you want a picture to accompany the article? If so, what would be in the picture? Would you want to quote someone? If so, who? What would you ask that person?

  If possible, do this planning exercise as a group project with several other writers.

1. Statement of the problem: _____

   _____

   _____

2. Strategies for personalizing the problem: _____

   _____

_____

_____

3. Plan of what would need to be done: _____

_____

_____

_____

_____

_____

Argument

Exercise 1

Included here are some hypothetical letters to the editors of national magazines in response to a variety of issues. Examine the arguments closely and characterize the means of persuasion, the types of premises and inferences, and the fallacies (if any) that are evident in the writers' arguments.

1. In response to a *Newsweek* article about nonsmokers' complaints about public smoking:

   > People talk about "rights," but it's beginning to seem that only smokers don't have them. Nonsmokers are fanatics with their holier-than-thou attitudes; they even take pleasure in being rude and militant. Smoking is a right —to do or not to do. Smokers should start fighting: if one right is taken away today, how many more tomorrow?

   Your description of this letter:

   _____

   _____

_____

_____

2. In response to a *Time* article about abortion:

> Women can't expect that legal means will bail them out. They need to
> determine—before they are pregnant—whether they want to have a child
> or not. When they are pregnant they have in effect decided. Women do not
> create life; they merely bear it. Thus they have no right to take it away.

Your description of this letter:

_____

_____

_____

_____

3. In response to a *Time* article about sod-busting (digging up and turning
   over natural grassland):

> We all know the developer types who look at the beautiful marshlands
> and say, "Gee, how lovely. We really appreciate the glories of nature."
> Then they turn around and destroy everything, putting up shopping malls
> and apartment complexes. Now it's happening in the West. Those farmers
> who profess to love the land are busily tearing it up and planting crops for
> which there is no market at all except the payment the Government makes
> —with our tax money.

Your description of this letter:

_____

_____

_____

_____

4. In response to a *U.S. News & World Report* article about drug abuse:

> Sure, Americans abuse drugs. They see such abuse daily on television; they watch their friends pop pills; they go to the stores where they can purchase nicotine, caffeine, sleeping pills, etc. And all this abuse is encouraged—even made possible—by the drug companies and advertising agencies and retailers—all those segments of society that profit from drug use. The step to using illegal drugs is a very short one.

Your description of this letter:

_____

_____

_____

_____

5. In response to a *Time* article on increased enlistment in the army:

> Young Americans should take advantage of what is offered them in these days of unemployment and expensive colleges. I think they should enroll in the military, where they can learn trades and be educated. I was a high school dropout when I joined the Air Force. Ten years later I'm an engineer.

Your description of this letter:

_____

_____

_____

_____

Exercise 2

In response to some magazine articles, readers have opposing views on the same subject. Read the following letters as you have been—examining the means of persuasion, the types of premises and inferences, and the fallacies (if any) that are evident in the writers' arguments. Then, compare the letters and decide which writer uses persuasion more effectively. Explain your answer.

In response to a *Newsweek* article about majoring in the humanities:

> Your article seemed to illustrate my life. My friends all sneered when I said I would major in classical Greek. Society doesn't need such dead pursuits, I was told; it needs people trained in technology, because technology is the future. Well, I am not a famous translator or an academic—in fact, I work in a software publishing firm. But I learned something about beauty and history and courage in my education; and those things are more useful to me than any mere technological skill will ever be, especially in a world where so few people understand them any longer.

Your description of this letter:

_____

_____

_____

_____

_____

> So who needs the Elgin Marbles or the operas of Mozart? People by the millions are starving all over the world. Why don't the highbrows go out and find a way to abolish hunger, rather than writing scholarly books that nobody understands?

Your description of this letter:

_____

_____

_____

_____

_____

Your comparison of the persuasion used in these two letters:

_____

_____

_____

_____

_____

_____

Exercise 3

In order to draw conclusions about a whole class after studying some of its members, you must make certain that the sample studied is typical of the entire class. The exercises included here offer you some practice in thinking about typical samples.

1. In each of the cases below decide if the sample is typical. If it isn't, how would you get a more typical one?
    a. Assume that you want to identify the most popular majors at one large university. If you were to stand outside of the electrical engineering building for two hours and ask every student coming out of the building what his or her major is, would your sample be typical? If not, where would you find a more typical sample of students to question?

    _____

    _____

    b. Assume that you want to determine whether Americans are aware of governmental problems in Central America. If you sent a questionnaire to 1,000 households in a large midwestern city, would your sample be typical? If not, what would you do to collect a representative sample for your questionnaire?

    _____

    _____

c. Assume that you are interested in knowing which televised sports have the largest viewing audience. If you surveyed a weekly TV guide and counted all the listings for televised sporting events that week in your city, would your sample be typical? If not, what would you do to collect a more representative sampling?

_____

_____

2. How would you gather a typical sample in order to draw conclusions that would answer the following questions?
    a. What do the students at your college consider to be the most important qualities of a good teacher?

_____

_____

    b. Assume that there is a vacant store a short distance from your apartment. What kind of business would be very likely to succeed if it moved into that store?

_____

_____

    c. How long is the average TV commercial on early evening network programs?

_____

_____

Exercise 4

Listed below are some average salary figures as shown in a 1983 U.S. Labor Department report. What conclusions can you draw from these figures? If possible, work with several other writers and try to draw at least five conclusions from these statistics.

Lawyers: law school graduates doing entry-level work—$28,119
          experienced high-level attorneys—$84,917
Engineers: beginners—$25,556
          those responsible for high-level projects—$66,938

Secretaries: range from $14,732 to $23,137
Computer programmers and analysts: range from $19,777 to $38,125
Personnel managers: lower-ranking job analysts—$19,894
                        high-ranking personnel directors—$62,645
File clerks: range from $9,702 to $13,699

What are some conclusions that you can draw from these figures?

_____

_____

_____

_____

_____

_____

_____

Exercise 5

Form a small group with several other writers in your class and assume
that you work in a small advertising agency. Your group is responsible for
thinking up a new product to launch on the market, planning an advertising campaign, and writing a short report for the board of directors. The
report must describe the product, justify it, and outline the ad campaign
(including a brief description of the audience, packaging, and emphasis in
the sales pitch). (Plan, draft, and write your report on other sheets of paper.)

    You are a member of the Board of Admissions for State University Med-
ical School. You have just concluded the personal interviews with appli-
cants for next year's entering class, and the Admissions Committee must
rank, in writing, all the students who were interviewed. When all the written
evaluations are collected, the committee will meet to decide which students will be admitted. You are beginning by looking over the notes you
took yesterday during interviews with two students, Molly Kess and Tim
Freeman. Read over your notes, write a two- or three-sentence summary
of your evaluation for each student, and then compare the students.

Molly Kess: had two summers experience as orderly on wards of county hospital; grades adequate, but not superior (generally a B+ average); says she only decided last year to go into medicine and began to study more seriously then; father is a dentist; enrolled in engineering when she first came to State University as a freshman; doesn't know what field of medicine she wants to specialize in; would prefer to attend Hoskins Medical School, but doesn't think she could get in; pleasant personality; speaks well; active in campus groups.

Tim Freeman: wants to help people and thus picked a service profession; mother is a doctor; maintained an A- average; seemed shy and uneasy during interview; was a chemistry major as an undergrad, but didn't know for the first few years what he would do after graduation; has sent applications to two other medical schools and doesn't have a strong preference for any one school (will enroll in whichever school admits him); no specific work experience in medical-related fields; spent one summer as a volunteer helper with a social work agency.

Your summary of Molly:

_____

_____

_____

_____

Your summary of Tim:

_____

_____

_____

_____

Your recommendation to the committee, comparing Molly and Tim (make clear which of the two you'd rank higher):

_____

_____

_____

_____

Exercise 6

The social studies department of your old high school is considering a request from some parents to add a unit on nuclear war to the curriculum. As the school board considers the matter, they are contacting a sample of graduates of the high school to gather their views. In the letter from the school board is a copy of a recent Associated Press newspaper article describing "Choices," the specific program under consideration.

The letter you have received has asked that you read the excerpts and write back to the board with your answers to the following questions:

1. Should a course on nuclear war be taught at your high school? Why?
2. If you think such a course should be taught, should materials from "Choices" be used? Why?

Included here is a copy of the newspaper article that was sent to you:

NEW ON THE SCHOOL CURRICULUM: WAR 101

WASHINGTON—It may be the hottest curriculum battle since sex education. Courses about nuclear war are proliferating in American schools, setting off debate over whether adolescents should dwell on the horrors of nuclear destruction.

Conservatives fear children are being taught one-sided, pacifist, doomsday dogma that serves only to weaken American resolve.

Liberal groups hope that exposing children to these issues in secondary schools will heighten public awareness of complex arms issues and eventually lay the groundwork for ridding the world of the threat of nuclear destruction.

Harry Chaucer, a science teacher at Champlain Valley High School in Hinesburg, Vt., says that last year he surveyed 100 students at Vergennes Union High School and found that more than half, "with no prompting whatsoever, described nuclear war as part of their future."

"Some students wrote entirely about nuclear war. Others would just say something like, 'If we survive nuclear war, then I'll have a Trans-Am (car) and a wife and a home' and the rest," he says.

In April, Chaucer helped the American Friends Service Committee organize a half-day of workshops on nuclear war at his school followed by a student vote on a nuclear freeze resolution. Thirty other schools across the state also cast ballots, with the students endorsing a mutual, verifiable freeze by almost 3 to 1.

With a nudge from the National Education Association and other groups alarmed about the arms race and increased U.S.-Soviet hostility, nuclear war courses have established a foothold in secondary schools, and moved from the tenuous status of the teach-in into the established curriculum on dozens of college campuses.

Cliff Kincaid, associate editor of Human Events, a conservative weekly newspaper, says the subject is fast becoming as controversial as sex education.

A generation ago, American schoolchildren learned to duck under their seats, heads on knees, in air raid drills that were supposed to help them survive a nuclear blast.

Today the students are in their seats, not under them, learning about throw-weights, megatonnage, ground zero, deterrence and the doctrine of "MAD"—mutually assured destruction.

Chaucer, 32, grew up in the 1950s and vividly remembers "the sirens going off and being told to hide under our desks. It seemed kind of a sparse response: putting our heads beneath our desks in response to what was supposed to be a mimicked nuclear attack."

The specter of a nuclear sword of Damocles may trouble today's youth more than it did their parents.

Drs. John E. Mack and William Beardslee, psychiatrists who teach at Harvard Medical School, concluded from a questionnaire that adolescents "are deeply disturbed about the threats of nuclear war and the risks of nuclear power."

Most of the school controversy has centered on "Choices: A Unit on Conflict and Nuclear War," a nuclear war course developed by the NEA and the Union of Concerned Scientists for junior high students.

Asked what he learned from "Choices," Jay Grossman, 13, a seventh grader at J. C. McKenna Middle School in Evansville, Wis., said, "Everybody thinks that Russia is the bad guy. We found out that the U.S.A. is just as bad because we're doing a lot of things like they are, like making nuclear weapons, like we dropped the first bomb . . . We got the whole thing started."

Classmate Nancy Jeans, 13, said, "We learned how many warheads we had and what our country is really doing . . . I think we should try to make an agreement with Russia. It's not right for us to blow each other up because we'll all be dead anyway, and nobody will win."

Their social studies teacher, Harold Beedle, 26, was among 47 junior high teachers in 34 states who tested "Choices" last fall.

After the four-week course, some of Beedle's students put anti-nuclear posters in the window of a local supermarket in the small town 20 miles south of Madison. Others wrote an 800-word article for the town newspaper, The Evansville Review, calling nuclear war "a definite nightmare" and urging talks to defuse U.S.-Soviet tensions.

That article created a two-month-long debate in the newspaper's letters columns, with one woman wondering "how could so much incorrect information (have) been absorbed by 12-year-old children" and others defending the course and its contents.

The Dover, Del., school board refused to allow teacher William Hutchinson to experiment with the course in one of its middle schools.

Natalie Goldring, an arms control analyst at the Union of Concerned Scientists who helped develop "Choices," says the course writers wanted to teach children about the nature of conflict and give them "a basic, factual understanding of nuclear weapons and nuclear war."

The $9.90 teaching guide shows a mock-up of the proposed 10-warhead MX missile, with one warhead containing 25 little "Hiroshima bombs" to show how much more destructive the MX would be than the bomb dropped on that Japanese city at the end of World War II. The Soviet SS-18, a missile comparable to the MX and that is already in the Soviet arsenal, is neither pictured nor mentioned.

The course briefly outlines nuclear and political developments since World War II. It includes first-person accounts from Hiroshima survivors, and a conflict resolution exercise on how to divvy up an unequal supply of M&M candies.

Of the controversy, Education Secretary T. H. Bell says, "I don't think it's right for a group of teachers to take a certain point of view and develop a curriculum on it and deliberately teach that view. I abhor that."

But Bell says it is possible for educators with strong personal convictions on controversial issues to teach objectively. "I wouldn't spend a lot of time away from the basics" to teach 12-year-olds about nuclear war, he adds, "but I'd just tell you that my son Peter is 12 years old and we have numerous discussions on this issue."

Kincaid, the Human Events editor, contends that the course "seemed designed to create a new generation of antinuclear activists."

The Washington Post, in an editorial, attacked such suggested student activities as finding out what goes on at local military bases and whether hometown colleges conduct weapons research. "This is not teaching in any normally accepted—or for that matter, acceptable—sense. It is political indoctrination," the paper said.

Albert Shanker, president of the American Federation of Teachers, also criticized "Choices." He wrote: "There's nothing wrong with the idea of helping teachers by making lesson plans available. Nor is it wrong to devote classroom time to conflict and nuclear war. What is wrong is a teachers union which has its own political views on these issues asking its members to fill their kids' heads with lopsided propaganda."

Terry Herndon, until recently the NEA's executive director and president of a coalition called Citizens Against Nuclear War, says, "We did not make any effort to present the whole truth about Soviet-American relationships or the whole truth about contemporary military balance in 10 easy lessons. To address all of those topics requires volumes."

Herndon says the information in "Choices" is "accurate (and) fairly objectively presented." Teachers seldom use an NEA curriculum as their only course material, he emphasizes.

"Never in my wildest moments did I expect that tens of thousands of teachers would take that book and go into the classroom and say, 'This is what we're going to do for the next 10 days.' That just doesn't happen," he says. "What we write as a resource guide for what we believe to be a relatively competent group of teachers they criticize as though it were a master plan for indoctrinating children, which it was never intended to be."

Ronny Sydney, a social studies teacher who taught "Choices" to freshmen at Brookline High School in Massachusetts, says, "It's somewhat biased. . . . It in some ways promotes a type of nuclear freeze."

John Furgione, a social studies teacher at Landis Middle School in Vineland, N.J., who also took part in the pilot testing of "Choices," says he tried to stay neutral, but "found myself most of the time playing the devil's advocate and coming up with a lot of viewpoints from the side that was different from what you would say the NEA is proposing."

Furgione adds, "If there are some things in there that some people would say a little bit promotes pacificity, which I don't think it does. . . . well, we better be sure we're doing that with kids and helping kids to understand that there are ways to solve their conflicts without resorting to a fight or gang warfare or something like that."

Other groups critical of Reagan's arms buildup also offer course guides, including Ground Zero and Educators for Social Responsibility. The Federation of American Scientists has a project to provide colleges with sample curricula. Another group, United Campuses to Prevent Nuclear War, a spin-off of the Union of Concerned Scientists, plays the same role.

Beedle, the teacher in Evansville, says the courses may reduce students' fears, not feed them.

Before "Choices," he says, "My kids basically had an exaggerated view about the destructiveness of nuclear weapons. . . . Most would say one nuclear weapon could destroy the entire world."

"They just had a lot of misinformation. I think it comes from parents and teachers who are not willing to talk about it because it seems too scary," he says. "We know it's bad and we don't want our kids to think about bad things, so we don't talk about it. And the kids end up developing their own ideas from the media." (Christopher Connell, "New on the School Curriculum: War 101," *The Lafayette Journal and Courier*)

Plan a draft of your response on scratch paper and then write, in the space provided, the letter that you intend to send to the board.

_____

_____

_____

_____

_____

_____

_____

_____

_____

If you can, ask a group of other writers to read your draft and offer suggestions for revising it so that you can send the best possible response to the board.

Write your revised version here:

_____

_____

_____

_____

_____

_____

_____

_____

_____

_____

11
The Essay Examination

RECOGNIZING KEY WORDS

Exercise 1

Included here are essay questions from several different fields of study. Underline any words in the question that indicate what the question is asking you to do, and then decide which of the key words listed below describes the kind of answer that is needed. Write the number of the key word or words on the line to the right. You might decide that more than one number belongs on that line.

1. compare
2. summarize
3. explain
4. evaluate
5. describe how something works or operates

a. What are three of the key factors involved in changing man's scientific view of the living world from a static Great Chain of Being to the Darwinian model of evolution through natural selection? _____

b. To aid students' learning, which is more effective, the use of meaningful material or frequent instruction? Why? _____

c. How do three of the major primates (presimian, monkey, and ape) differ on the basis of their adaptive characteristic trends? Include information on locomotion, anatomy, development of special senses, and social organization. _____

d. If Company X receives a bill on April 15 for $3,300, for repairing their computers, and if payment is due on April 25, should they make a journal entry on April 15

to record an expense and an account payable, or should
they make no entry until the check is returned with the
bank statement in early May? Which is the better procedure and why?   _____

e. How is the surplus feedgrain situation related to live-
stock producers' decisions?   _____

f. How do national surveys, such as the Harris Poll and the
Nielsen ratings, sample public opinion?   _____

g. Compare the emphasis on respect for authority among
the working class and among the upper class, in industrialized societies.   _____

h. It is generally agreed among agricultural experts that
agriculture's problem today is not one of overproduc-
tion but rather one of lack of demand. What are some
reasons that Americans might be "under-consuming"?
Why?   _____

i. If you were a clinician helping a person to overcome
stuttering, would you offer positive reinforcement or
negative reinforcement? Why?   _____

j. How are a small company's assets and liabilities determined?   _____

k. Name and discuss the effectiveness of three epigramma-
tic dicta of Horace.   _____

l. In *Walden*, against what does Thoreau direct his social
criticism?   _____

Exercise 2

Applications for jobs, college entrance, service organizations (such as student government offices and college honoraries), and the like often ask for
essay answers. Browse through some forms and use the space provided below to copy the questions that an applicant should respond to in essay
form. Underline the key words in the question that indicate what is required in the answer.

1. _____

_____

_____

2. _____

_____

_____

3. _____

_____

_____

4. _____

_____

_____

Exercise 3

Which sentences belong in an answer to each of these questions? Answer yes or no for each sentence that follows the essay question.

1. Compare the history of astrology with the history of astronomy.

	Yes	No
a. Astrology and astronomy were not distinguished as separate fields until about the sixth century.	____	____
b. Based on a system they devised to read the stars, Babylonian priests set dates for religious ceremonies.	____	____
c. Although Hitler's regime condemned astrology, at the end of World War II, Hitler consulted astrologers regularly.	____	____
d. While astronomy flourished in the Middle Ages with the discoveries by Galileo and Kepler, the pagan gods associated with astrology led the Church to condemn astrology. As a result, astrology declined in popularity.	____	____
e. The mythology of the Greeks and Romans is said to be derived from astrology.	____	____
f. King Umberto of Italy, when introduced to a businessman who resembled him greatly, was astonished to find that they had exactly the same birth date and time.	____	____

2. How successful was the Framingham Heart Study Project in identifying causes of heart disease?

	Yes	No
a. The Heart Study Project has studied the inhabitants of Framingham for over thirty years.	____	____
b. The findings of the Heart Study Project have confirmed the links between heart disease and such factors as overweight, lack of exercise, and large intake of high-cholesterol foods.	____	____
c. The goal of the Heart Study Project is to discover all the factors that increase people's risk of dying from heart disease.	____	____
d. The most pervasive health problem in the United States today is not cancer but cardiovascular disease.	____	____
e. After extensive study, the medical researchers in the Heart Study Project have affirmed the link between lipoproteins and heart disease.	____	____
f. As demonstrated by the people of Framingham, the more air people can suck into their lungs, the longer they live. In other words, Framingham residents with poor lung capacity tend to die young.	____	____

3. Discuss the controversy surrounding the use of artificial turf versus real grass in sports arenas and explain the advantages and disadvantages of each.

a. Pioneered in the mid-sixties by the Monsanto Corporation, nylon artificial turf now covers more than 300 playing fields around the world.	____	____
b. Many athletes blame artificial turf for tendonitis, abrasions, shin splints, and broken bones.	____	____
c. When players first play on artificial turf, they have to adjust their playing because, as some athletes insist, it causes balls to bounce higher and runners to run faster.	____	____
d. Astroturf is made of nylon fibers that are tightly stitched into a woven mat. The mat is laid over a foam pad for cushioning and then glued to an asphalt base.	____	____
e. While grass has all the numerous problems of any other common ground cover, artificial turf also wears out from smog, dust, and radiation.	____	____
f. Recent innovations in the construction of artificial turf allow it to drain more efficiently and keep it from becoming matted down.	____	____

PLANNING ESSAY EXAM ANSWERS

Exercise 1

Read the following excerpts and then read the essay questions that follow each selection. Plan your answers in the space provided below the question. You may make an outline or just jot down some notes, but do not write out the complete answer. Instead, use this exercise to practice planning answers.

These excerpts are from a report on human memory:

> Traditional learning and memory specialists have argued that memory functions much like a computerized tape recorder. In their view, forgetting is simply the mismanagement of our capacity to retrieve information stored permanently somewhere in our brains. The courts generally rely on this concept of the reliability of memory. In fact, the sanctity of citizen testimony, which depends on it, is the bulwark of Western jurisprudence.
>
> But . . . memories are impermanent, fragile, and easily undermined. Forensic psychologist Robert Buckhout, who has testified in 70 trials, agrees. "Uncritical acceptance of eyewitness testimony," he says, "seems to be based on the fallacious notion that the human observer is a perfect recording device—that everything that passes before his or her eyes is recorded and can be pulled out by sharp questioning or refreshing one's memory. . . . This is impossible—human perception and memory function effectively by being selective. A human being has no particular need for perfect recall; perception and memory are decision-making processes affected by the totality of a person's abilities, background, environment, attitudes, motives, and beliefs, and by the methods used in testing recollection of people and events."
>
> "No matter how well meaning or how well trained observers are," [Elizabeth] Loftus says, "there are ways to make people see, hear, and even smell things that never were." Memory doesn't fade, she says, it grows. "What may fade is the initial perception, the actual experience of the events. But every time we recall an event we must reconstruct the memory, and so each time it is changed—colored by succeeding events, increased understanding, a new context, suggestions by others, other people's recollections. We can get people to conjure up details that are pure fantasy. With the right conditions, we can probably convince someone that green is blue or that the chicken he had for dinner last night was roast beef." . . .
>
> But the data on the malleability of memory are piling up. If recognition and memory were passive, if our brains videotaped our experiences and put them in permanent storage, experimenters should be able to retrieve what was originally encoded in the brain.

But they can't. Even if people are warned that misleading information may have been presented to them, they still don't reject that in favor of what really happened. Once a person incorporates misinformation into his memory, he is apparently unable to recover the unadulterated event. . . .

Results . . . seem to confirm that memory is fragile, and new information changes it. However, not all researchers agree. Psychologist John Morton . . . believes there is no loss of the original memory; it is there somewhere in the brain. The closer one gets to recreating the conditions that existed at the time the original memory formed, the easier it is to gain access to it. Over the years other proponents of permanent memory storage have tried all sorts of deep retrieval systems to try to tease out the original memory, with varying degrees of success. Freud, of course, based his theory of psychoanalysis on being able to retrieve childhood memories. (Joann Ellison Rodgers, "The Malleable Memory of Eyewitnesses," *Science 82*)

Question: How reliable is human memory? How does new or false information affect memory? If there are conflicting views, include these in your discussion.

_____

_____

_____

_____

_____

_____

_____

_____

This excerpt assesses the nature and impact of the War of the Falkland Islands, 1982:

The War of the Falkland Islands began with a successful invasion by Argentine forces on April 2, 1982, and ended with their surrender to British forces ten weeks later. It was a textbook example of a limited war—limited in time, in location, in objectives and in means. Care was taken when it came to the treatment of civilians and prisoners and only in the later stages did noncombatants get caught in the fighting. The military casualties were severe—800 to 1,000 Argentine and 250 British dead—but still only a small proportion of the forces committed.

In the character of the military operations, the clarity of the issues at stake and the unambiguous outcome, it was a curiously old-fashioned war. We have become used to wars of political complexity and strategic confusion. Such modern dramas were underway in the Middle East and Central America in 1982, compared with which the Falklands War came and went like something from the Victorian stage: a simple plot, a small but well-defined cast of characters, a story in three acts with a clear beginning, middle and end, and a straightforward conclusion that everybody could understand.

The limited and old-fashioned nature of the war should caution against trying to draw too much of wider significance out of the experience. Nevertheless, in an age of rapid technological development without regular opportunities to assess the current state of the military art, the details of any war will be picked over by those anxious for guidance on how to prepare for future conflicts. Professional observers expected much from this conflict: two belligerents capable of using advanced military technology properly and, there was reason to believe, the first major sea battles since 1945. (Lawrence Freedman, "The War of the Falkland Islands, 1982" *Foreign Affairs*)

Question: Why is the War of the Falkland Islands, 1982, considered a limited and "curiously old-fashioned war"? Explain the use of this term by identifying at least three factors that substantiate this description.

_____

_____

_____

_____

_____

_____

_____

The following excerpt discusses the problem of "orphan drugs," drugs that manufacturers are reluctant to develop and market because they are only needed by a small percentage of the population.

Orphan drugs fall into two categories: those that have been developed but are no longer manufactured and, as is more often the case, those that never make it to market because their low profit potential does not justify the cost of testing and development. . . .

There is no universal agreement as to who or what is chiefly to blame. In the view of many drug companies and sick people, it is not the pharmaceutical industry but the Food and Drug Administration that is the major villain. Although the F.D.A. puts the cost of a new medicine at $7.3 million, drug manufacturers say that in reality they can expect to spend up to $74 million to get a new drug to market. Both price tags cover the difficult clinical testing procedures demanded by government standards, but unlike the F.D.A., the pharmaceutical firms also consider the accompanying high cost of overhead and research dead ends. In addition, animal testing, literature searches, and various phases of human testing can take from five to 10 years, the F.D.A. and the drug companies agree. . . .

[C]ritics . . . argue that drug companies would like nothing better than to have the safety and effectiveness of *all* prescription medicines eased in the name of orphan diseases. In their view, the firms could well afford to make more orphans without such special concessions. Until 1980 the pharmaceutical industry was the nation's most profitable, and since then has been surpassed only by the tobacco, oil, and some service industries. . . .

Skeptics also question an assertion that has been made by Thomas Althuis, manager of scientific affairs for the drug company Pfizer, Inc. In a letter recently published in the *New England Journal of Medicine,* Althuis says that the alleged indifference of the industry to the orphan drug problem is "folklore" and "a myth." He reported that 30 firms, including his own, have developed and marketed "over 40" unprofitable drugs as a public service since 1970. His critics question that number and point out that in addition there are thousands of remaining orphan diseases still languishing without funds because they lack financial promise. Althuis counters that the real culprits are F.D.A. inflexibility and "a lack of knowledge about the biology and chemistry of most rare diseases" that makes it difficult to design appropriate therapy. . . .

The F.D.A. has a mixed record on orphan drugs. In some cases of required testing the agency has been justifiably charged with foot dragging and bureaucratic bungling. But though the Pharmaceutical Manufacturers Association has petitioned the F.D.A. to consider more foreign data, the government occasionally accepts the results of foreign tests, as they did when considering the drug Blocadren, first developed in Norway for prevention of second heart attacks.

Even for the drug with financial promise, F.D.A. requirements are arduous and costly. About 1,000 human testing applications are approved each year. Very few, in fact, are turned down. But only about 100 make it through the final approval phase each year. The F.D.A. tries to speed the approval process by allowing limited use of life-saving drugs while testing is in progress. J. Richard Crout, former director of F.D.A.'s Bureau of Drugs, told a congressional hearing last year that his agency "has a long-standing policy of approving [new drugs] on the basis of studies with relatively few patients when the disease in question is rare and the benefit-risk considerations are clearly favorable. . . . In general, our policy is to apply the fundamental standards of safety and effectiveness, plus a bit of flexibility and common sense." (Judith Randal, "Up for Adoption: Rare Drugs for Rare Diseases," *Science 82*)

Question: What is the orphan drug problem? Compare the key issues in the debate between the drug companies who should be developing and marketing these drugs and their critics who say they are not meeting their obligation to do so.

_____

_____

_____

_____

_____

_____

_____

The next excerpt discusses the agricultural revolution in Third World countries:

Before the 1920s, change in American agriculture was slow. Silent films of the time wonderfully record the dusty dirt roads, farm wagons and Model-T Fords passing by, threshers in overalls pitching bundles, small family farms with cows, pigs, and chickens, and the speed and power of a rural way of life set by the three-mile-an-hour gait of the horse. By 1940, as highly mechanized, highly capitalized farming took over, this way of life was just a nostalgic memory. Since 1940 the number of Americans who farm has dropped from about 30 percent to less than three percent. This is probably the most fundamental change in modern American history. Its cultural consequences have still to be calculated.

If the 1920s and 1930s brought decisive change to American agriculture, the decade of the 1970s now is likely to be seen, if at a much lower level of technology, as the start of a similar turning point for many of the people of the Third World, particularly the Asians. . . .

One can now confidently say that a quiet agricultural revolution has begun in the Third World that is likely to have more dramatic effects on more human beings than any revolution that has gone before. This agricultural revolution differs from our own in three fundamental ways:

First, it is coming 50 years later. During these 50 years, man's control over matter and energy, particularly in physics and biology, and his ability to process and distribute this knowledge, has grown enormously. As Vernon Ruttan and other agricultural economists have pointed out, the biggest gains in American farm production have come from oil-based mechanical technology, or advances in output per worker. Between 1920 and 1940, horses were quite suddenly replaced by tractors, combines and other machines, with new investment also in fertilizer, electricity, prepared feeds, pesticides and other nonfarm inputs. In the Third World, starting about 1967–68, the biggest gains in farm production have come from biological technology, advances in output per unit of land. The numbers of draft animals—about 75 million in India, 50 million in China (which uses more river junks)—are not declining, but growing with official encouragement. Biotechnology, unlike mechanical technology, does not demand the same substitution of capital for labor. Experience in Asia during the 1970s shows it is more labor intensive, not less.

Second, peasants are involved, that is, subsistence cultivators within ancient civilizations. Their culture is highly dependent upon a village, the basic economic unit. There are about two million of these villages left, a third of them still pretty much intact in post-Mao China, another third in what was pre-1947 India—India, Pakistan and Bangladesh—and the rest scattered among the other 130 or so nations of Asia, Africa and Latin America, plus some islands. North America, unlike Europe or Russia, never had a peasant society. The uprooted European peasant immigrants, who mostly settled America's post-frontier rural society, found themselves in scattered, individual farms surrounding a small town usually dominated by a Yankee commercial and professional class. Peasant tradition was discouraged; farming was seen as a business for profit, with land, rent and labor looked upon as capital and commodity. As post-1940 agriculture industrialized and farms got even bigger and fewer, thousands of small farm communities died or moved toward extinction, and with them their churches and schools. Despite pro-rural feelings among presidents from Thomas Jefferson to Theodore Roosevelt to John F. Kennedy, the economic basis of American culture, never having been a village, shifted from small town to city. This has meant a weakening of church, family, the work ethic and the small town's sense of community. It suggests the American model is not one the Third World can or should follow.

Third, the staggeringly big populations involved are way beyond our own experience. Village populations have been doubling every 30 years, though, since contraceptives started to catch on, that interval has grown slightly to 34 years. In a few places—the Nile Valley, the Mexican central highlands, the island of Java—absolute population growth has already over-shot the available land and water even with the maximum application of known biotechnology. Here an alternative to agriculture must be found, probably in decentralized industry. Japan offers the best model; it indus-trialized through a system of small village-based engineering workshops which made components for a central core factory (as American bomber pilots discovered during World War II). At the Indonesian government's re-quest, the Japanese are now trying to transplant their system to Java as a way of keeping people on the land. (Richard Critchfield, "Science and the Villager: The Last Sleeper Wakes," *Foreign Affairs*)

Question: How is the agricultural revolution of the 1970s in the Third World different from the American agricultural revolution of the 1920s and 1930s?

_____

_____

_____

_____

_____

_____

_____

Exercise 2

Assume that you are a teacher in a humanities course (you can specify the department or field of study), and you have assigned your students to read the following excerpts from an essay on the F.B.I.'s plan to computerize criminal records. Read the excerpts and then plan the essay exam you would give your students by answering the questions that follow the essay.

[T]he Interstate Identification Index is part of an F.B.I. drive to vastly enlarge the scope and purpose of a 16-year-old communications network that already links tens of thousands of state and local criminal-justice agencies.

The primary purpose of the project is to devise a national communications system through which a policeman in New York, a prosecutor in Chicago or a judge in Los Angeles will be able to determine swiftly whether the suspects they are holding have ever been arrested in any other state.

The F.B.I. and most law enforcement officials are convinced that speeding the exchange of information about an individual's past contacts with the criminal-justice system through such a network will reduce crime. . . .

Law-enforcement officials argue that instant access to the records of a suspect's criminal past will help them to decide quickly whether to arrest a suspect, or to identify the most likely suspect from a group of suspects, and will help judges to set adequate bail for defendants who may have serious records in other states.

In addition, as one Michigan law-enforcement official recently told the F.B.I., the system would protect the lives of policemen. Speaking of a case, the official said: "The record indicated the subject had been arrested and convicted in Florida of two assaults, one of a police officer. This information and any information of like nature which may come back upon inquiry is without doubt of great value and benefit to officers in the field."

Experienced law-enforcement officials acknowledge, however, that the rapid transmission of criminal-history records may be less helpful than is commonly thought. For one thing, a majority of violent criminals do not move from state to state. Also, many criminals are apprehended as a result of testimony by their victims or by bystanders, rather than by the information on their records.

Moreover, a number of criminal-justice officials, members of Congress and former White House computer experts are worried that, besides not providing a panacea for the crime problem, the F.B.I. plan could upset the constitutionally established balance of power between the states and the Federal Government, could improperly deny people jobs and could encroach upon civil liberties. . . .

Since the earliest days of American history, law enforcement has been a profoundly local business. Sheriffs are still locally elected in most parts of the United States. So are district attorneys. Most criminal acts are defined by state legislatures and most criminals are sentenced by state or local judges according to the mandate of state laws. Even the F.B.I. is aware that a national communications system that explicitly empowers the bureau to force local and state agencies to meet Federal standards of accuracy and completeness would somewhat modify the fundamental structure of government laid down by the Constitution.

The second concern centered on questions about the records that would be transmitted by the network. Would the increased distribution of records that frequently are incomplete or inaccurate reduce the efficiency of the police? Would these records reduce the opportunity for a fair trial? Would the growing use of these records by employers and others outside the criminal-justice system, a practice common now in many states, lead to situations in which individuals turned to crime because they were unjustifiably denied a job?

The third concern involved a question about the combined impact of the proposed communications network and the masses of information contained in the data bases of the states. Could such a system be used to keep track of citizens who are not criminals? (David Burnham, "How Long Should the Arm of the Law Be?" *New York Times Magazine*)

1. What are the important points that you want your students to remember?

   _____

   _____

   _____

   _____

2. What two essay questions might you ask on the exam?

   a. _____

   _____

   _____

   b. _____

   _____

3. What key words in your questions indicate what is required?

   a. _____

   b. _____

4. Outline the key points you would want in the answer.

_____

_____

_____

_____

_____

_____

WRITING ANSWERS

Clip a news article from a magazine such as *Time*, *Newsweek*, or *U.S. News and World Report*. Formulate an essay question that might appear in an exam on this reading and then answer the question you posed.

1. Clip article here: _____

_____

_____

_____

_____

_____

Essay question: _____

_____

_____

Your answer: _____

_____

_____

_____

_____

_____

_____

_____

Using a textbook from a course in which you are likely to take an essay exam, summarize the contents of a short section on one particular topic. Then pose two probable essay questions that a teacher might ask about the information in your summary and answer one of those questions.

The topic: _____

Your summary: _____

_____

_____

_____

Two possible essay exam questions on this topic:

1. _____

   _____

   _____

2. _____

   _____

   _____

Your essay answer to one of those questions:

_____

_____

12
The Critical Essay

At the end of this chapter there are drawings by Jules Feiffer and Gary Trudeau, short stories by two well-known authors, Mario Pei and James Thurber—and one by a college student, Peter Peregrine. These selections will be used with some of the practice exercises offered here.

ELEMENTS OF IMAGINATIVE WRITING

Situation

Exercise 1

In the excerpts included below examine the way each author introduces the circumstances or setting from which the action of the story will emerge. As you read each selection, ask yourself how the situation is revealed. Use the space below each excerpt to answer the following questions: How does the author use description, explanation, or dialogue to reveal the situation? What is the situation? Given this situation, what do you think the plot will focus on?

THE STOLEN BACILLUS

This again," said the Bacteriologist, slipping a glass slide under the microscope, "is a preparation of the celebrated Bacillus of Cholera—the cholera germ."

The pale-faced main peered down the microscope. He was evidently not accustomed to that kind of thing, and held a limp white hand over his disengaged eye. "I see very little," he said.

"Touch this screw," said the Bacteriologist; "perhaps the microscope is out of focus for you. Eyes vary so much. Just the fraction of a turn this way or that."

"Ah! now I see," said the visitor. "Not so very much to see, after all. Little streaks and shreds of pink. And yet those little particles, those mere atomies, might multiply and devastate a city! Wonderful!"

He stood up, and releasing the glass slip from the microscope, held it in his hand towards the window. "Scarcely visible," he said, scrutinising the preparation. He hesitated. "Are these—alive? Are they dangerous now?"

"Those have been stained and killed," said the Bacteriologist. "I wish, for my own part, we could kill and stain every one of them in the universe."

"I suppose," the pale man said with a slight smile, "that you scarcely care to have such things about you in the living—in the active state?"

"On the contrary, we are obliged to," said the Bacteriologist. "Here, for instance—" He walked across the room and took up one of several sealed tubes. "Here is the living thing. This is a cultivation of the actual living disease bacteria." He hesitated. "Bottled cholera, so to speak." (H. G. Wells)

_____

_____

_____

_____

_____

_____

ONE HUNDRED DOLLAR BILL

The new one hundred dollar bill, clean and green, freshening the heart with the colour of springtime, slid over the glass of the teller's counter and passed under his grille to a fat hand, dingy on the knuckles, but brightened by a flawed diamond. This interesting hand was a part of one of those men who seem to have too much fattened muscle for their clothes; his shoulders distended his overcoat; his calves strained the sprightly checked cloth, a little soiled, of his trousers; his short neck bulged above the glossy collar. His hat, round and black as a pot and appropriately small, he wore slightly obliqued, while under its curled brim his small eyes twinkled surreptitiously between those upper and nether puffs of flesh that mark the too faithful practitioner of unhallowed gaieties. Such was the first individual owner of the new one hundred dollar bill, and he at once did what might have been expected of him.

Moving away from the teller's grille, he made a cylindrical packet of bills smaller in value—"ones" and "fives"—then placed round them, as a wrapper, the beautiful one hundred dollar bill, snapped a rubber band over it; and the desired inference was plain; a roll all of hundred dollar bills, inside as well as outside. Something more was plain, too: obviously the man's small head had a sportive plan in it, for the twinkle between his eye puffs hinted of liquor in the offing and lively women impressed by a show of masterly riches. Here, in brief, was a man who meant to make a night of it, who would feast, dazzle, compel deference and be loved. For money gives power, and power is loved; no doubt he would be loved. He was happy, and went out of the bank believing that money made for joy. (Booth Tarkington)

_____

_____

_____

_____

_____

TWO BLUE BIRDS

There was a woman who loved her husband, but she could not live with him. The husband, on his side, was sincerely attached to his wife, yet he could not live with her. They were both under forty, both handsome, and both attractive. They had the most sincere regard for one another, and felt, in some odd way, eternally married to one another. They knew each other more intimately than they knew anybody else, they felt more known to one another than to any other person. (D. H. Lawrence)

_____

_____

_____

_____

Exercise 2

To see whether the situation of a literary work is important to the total
work, consider what the work would be like if the situations were different. Read the following descriptions of a few well-known characters and
places with a suggested change in the situations. What would be gained or
lost? Which is more effective—the situation in the original work or the
suggested version? Write your own answers in the space provided, then
think of your own "what if" and ask another writer to answer the same
questions about your example.

1. What if Bugs Bunny were a huge grizzly bear (Bugs Bear) and Elmer
   Fudd was still the same little man out hunting him?

   _____

   _____

   _____

   _____

2. What if Romeo, in Shakespeare's *Romeo and Juliet*, were a wealthy
   young twentieth-century American male studying at an Ivy League college and Juliet were an attractive 18-year-old who recently immigrated
   to the United States with her family because of poverty and famine in
   her native land?

   _____

   _____

   _____

3. What if Henry David Thoreau's Walden Pond were a California state
   park (located twenty miles south of Disneyland) and charged admission
   fees?

   _____

   _____

_____

_____

Add your own example:

4. _____

_____

_____

_____

_____

_____

Exercise 3

In Mario Pei's short story "With His Arm in a Sling," included at the end of this chapter, what if Tommy were a burglar attempting to break into a bank and the man with his arm in a sling were the night watchman at the bank? Could the story still have the same plot? What effect would the change of situation have on the characters and the theme?

Character

Exercise 1

Select a recent movie that you've seen and list one major and one minor
character in the movie to describe. As you plan your character description,
ask yourself the following questions and use the space provided to take
planning notes.

What adjectives would you use to describe the person? How were these
characteristics revealed—by what the person said, by how the person
acted, by the way in which other characters acted toward this person,
or by what they said about the person? Include at least one specific
example for each adjective.

What is the character like at the beginning of the story? How do you know
this? Does the character change as the story progresses? If so, what is
the change and is it justified?

Title of the movie: _____

Major character: _____

Planning notes: _____

_____

_____

_____

Description: _____

_____

_____

_____

Minor character: _____

Planning notes: _____

_____

_____

_____

Description: _____

_____

_____

_____

_____

Exercise 2

Briefly describe as many as you can of the following characters. Then add five more characters to the list and describe them briefly also.

1. Lucy (in the Peanuts cartoon strip) _____

_____

_____

2. Gatsby (in F. Scott Fitzgerald's *The Great Gatsby*) _____

_____

_____

_____

3. Mary Poppins _____

_____

_____

4. The lieutenant (in John Fowles's *The French Lieutenant's Woman*) ___

_____

_____

_____

5. Miss Marple (in Agatha Christie's mystery stories) _____

_____

_____

_____

6. Lady Macbeth (in Shakespeare's *Macbeth*) _____

_____

_____

_____

7. Cinderella _____

_____

_____

8. Holden Caulfield (in J. D. Salinger's *Catcher in the Rye*) _____

_____

_____

9. Mr. Spock (in *Star Trek*) _____

_____

_____

10. Christopher Robin (in *Winnie-the-Pooh*) _____

_____

_____

Add your own characters to describe:

11. _____

_____

_____

_____

12. _____

_____

_____

_____

13. _____

_____

_____

_____

14. _____

_____

_____

_____

15. _____

_____

_____

_____

Exercise 3

How do you learn about the main characters in Thurber's two short fables
included at the end of this chapter? Is this similar to or different from the
way in which the main character is revealed in the other short stories?
Explain.

_____

_____

_____

_____

_____

_____

Read the short story by Mario Pei included at the end of this chapter, and
study the cartoons by Gary Trudeau and Jules Feiffer. What methods does
Pei use to describe the characters in his story? How do Trudeau and Feiffer
reveal the characters in their drawings? What are some of the similarities
and differences among all three authors' methods of character description?
Of the characters who speak, which sound authentic or consistent with the
kind of people they are supposed to be?

_____

_____

_____

Plot and Dramatic Conflict

The first exercise in this chapter presents the beginnings of three short stories. Select one story to finish. Form a small group with several other writers and ask yourselves the following questions, which should help you to write an appropriate conclusion for the story. (This conclusion need not be similar to the original one used by the author.) What is the situation? How does the situation influence the story? Describe the characters and consider patterns of behavior that they would be likely to exhibit as the story moves forward. How much of the plot is evident so far? What opposing forces are there that will create a dramatic conflict? How might the conflict be resolved? When your group has answered these questions and made some planning notes for the conclusion, write a summary of the ending together. If possible, compare your ending with one written by another group. Are both valid endings for the story?

Story selected: _____

Planning notes: _____

_____

_____

_____

_____

A brief summary of your ending: _____

_____

_____

_____

_____

_____

Theme

Exercise 1

What are the themes in the drawings by Jules Feiffer and Gary Trudeau found at the end of this chapter?

Feiffer: _____

_____

_____

Trudeau: _____

_____

_____

Exercise 2

Some themes are universal and embedded in many different situations and plots. Drawing on books, plays, and movies, think of two examples that illustrate each of the themes listed below. If possible, form a small group to answer this question.

1. Growing up is a painful but enlightening experience.

    Example 1: _____

    Example 2: _____
2. The good guy usually wins in the end.

    Example 1: _____

    Example 2: _____
3. Totalitarian governments may come to rule the world and control every-one in the society.

    Example 1: _____

    Example 2: _____

4. Wealth and power can't ensure happiness.

    Example 1: _____

    Example 2: _____

5. If earth's natural resources aren't protected, dire consequences will
follow.

    Example 1: _____

    Example 2: _____

What is the theme of the story by Mario Pei?

_____

_____

_____

_____

What is the theme of the story by Peter Peregrine?

_____

_____

_____

_____

Structure

In the story by Mario Pei, the main character recalls past events. How necessary is this to the structure of the story?

_____

_____

_____

_____

_____

_____

_____

What is the structure of Peter Peregrine's story? At the beginning and end of the story the boy is in a house. How does this contribute to the structure of the story?

_____

_____

_____

_____

_____

_____

_____

_____

Symbols

Exercise 1

Listed here are some closed symbols, symbols that stand for only one thing. What do these five symbols stand for? After explaining them, add five of your own and ask another writer to explain what they stand for.

1. In an intersection on a major street, a flashing red light _____

   _____

2. A referee at a football game raising both arms straight in the air _____

   _____

   _____

3. A skull and crossbones on a bottle filled with chemicals _____

   _____

4. A TV or film director who runs a finger horizontally across his throat

   _____

   _____

5. In a restaurant, two signs on two different doors next to each other, one
   with a silhouette of a woman and the other with a silhouette of a man

   _____

   _____

   Your examples of closed symbols:

6. _____

   _____

7. _____

   _____

8. _____

   _____

9. _____

   _____

10. _____

_____

Exercise 2

Listed here are five open symbols, symbols that can be interpreted differently by different people. What interpretation would you offer for the symbols listed here? After writing an interpretation for these, list five more open symbols and ask another writer to explain what the symbols stand for. Are the other writer's interpretations the same as yours?

1. A Christmas tree _____

_____

_____

2. Tomb of the Unknown Soldier in Arlington National Cemetery in

Virginia _____

_____

_____

3. A wedding ring _____

_____

_____

4. A red carpet rolled out for someone to use _____

_____

_____

5. A "punk" haircut _____

_____

Your examples of open symbols:

6. _____

_____

_____

7. _____

_____

_____

8. _____

_____

_____

9. _____

_____

_____

10. _____

_____

_____

Exercise 3

The excerpt included below uses numerous symbols for the subway. List some of them and explain what aspect of the subway they stand for.

A RIDE ON THE NEW YORK SUBWAY

Each working day of their lives, millions of New Yorkers "willingly" descend hundreds of feet, through huge manholes in the street, into a subterranean world of darkness and gloom; there, in the dimness, they crowd mechanically together in astonishing numbers at the edge of a deep pit riven with tracks of steel fatal to the human touch, along which will hurtle with exhausting irregularity an iron monster spitting flame and noise like some pagan construction designed for the express purpose of intimidating the cowering human; when the monster comes to a temporary halt, doors slide open in its sides, and the men and women at the edge of the pit tumble inside, very much like Jonah tumbling into the whale; the doors then lock shut, and the iron creature goes roaring off down the pitch-black tunnel with its cargo of human prisoners—sullen penitents all: confused, silent, passive-aggressives doomed to an hour or more of suffocating companionship. . . . (Vivian Gornick, "A Ride on the New York Subway," originally printed in *The Village Voice*, December 21, 1972; reprinted in *The Village Voice Anthology (1956–1980)*, edited by Geoffrey Stokes)

Irony

Exercise 1

In contrast to what is overtly stated in the situations described below, what is really meant? After answering the question in relation to 1 and 2, make up a situation of your own and ask another writer to explain what is really meant.

1. In a congressional debate, a Senator compliments one of his opponents by saying, "My distinguished colleague has certainly attempted to do his best to help the drought-plagued farmers of our nation, and I am sure he has thought long and hard about what kind of bill to offer. He undoubtedly even meant well." What is the Senator really saying about the merit of the bill?

   _____

   _____

   _____

2. A movie critic might praise Clint Eastwood's performance in his latest movie by saying that Eastwood is so consistent that he is always Eastwood no matter what the role or what the story. No script or director will ever be able to make him into any other person. Do you think the critic is really praising the actor's consistency, or is that reviewer suggesting something else? If so, what?

_____

_____

_____

3. A situation of your own:

_____

_____

_____

_____

_____

Exercise 2

Assume that you are writing a story about a young boy who leaves home to search for a better life, winds up in California, becomes wealthy because of some slightly illegal land deals, and then spends much of his time trying to avoid federal government agents investigating him for possible tax evasion. When some angry underworld characters also begin to hunt him down because he has invaded their territory, he returns to his small town in Texas. There he finds his older brother leading the reasonably contented life of a not very prosperous feed and grain salesman. If you were looking for an ironic twist to this story, which of the following endings would you choose? Explain your answer.

1. He decides to stay in his home town and settle down, hoping that he won't be found there by the people who are chasing him.
2. He leaves his home town suddenly in the middle of the night because he fears that he will be tracked down and bring trouble to his family. He is last seen wandering homeless and rootless in a large East Coast city.
3. The older brother, hearing about his high lifestyle, asks for a loan so that he, too, can go off to California and start a better life. Hoping that, because of their strong family resemblance, his older brother will be mistaken for him, the main character gives the older brother his

California company, which turns out to have become highly successful in his absence. The older brother pays off the back taxes, reaches a peaceful agreement with the criminals, and becomes a prosperous land-owner.

Which ending would you choose? Why? _____

_____

_____

_____

Point of View and Voice

Exercise 1

In each of the selections included here, the point of view is different. Is the author omniscient—in other words, does he or she know everything that the subjects are thinking, know what will happen in the future, and so on? Is the author's view limited only to what one person knows? Or is there some combination of the two? Compare the three uses of point of view and their relevance to the story being told. Consider also the author's voice. Is the story written in first person (the "I" voice) or in third person? How does this influence the story?

> Childhood, it seems to me now, is a continuous interchange of hiding the secrets and telling.
> Don't tell! we whispered then.
> Don't tell Mommy, I hear my son, haughty and brazen, whisper now to his brother, and I, hurt to be so left out, hurry away from their door and hide in the kitchen.
> Tell us! we demanded, chins pointed out defiantly, trying to dispel the chant of "Don't tell the children," the sudden transformation of enticing, comprehensible English into musical, strange Yiddish. Never had the time to teach us Yiddish, they said, but the truth was crystal clear. Often I wish my husband and I could converse in French, pig-Latin, anything rather than waiting until 8:30 to say certain things. (Jane Lazarre, "Growing up Red: Remembering a Communist Childhood in New York," *The Village Voice Anthology (1956-1980)*, edited by Geoffrey Stokes)

Your comments on point of view and voice in this selection: _____

_____

_____

_____

_____

Day by day the plague increased. The summer sun blazed down on the town; no drop of rain fell; no breath of wind stirred. The corpses rotting in the houses and the corpses carelessly buried bred a stench, which permeated the motionless atmosphere of the streets and attracted swarms and clouds of ravens and crows, until the walls and roofs were black with them. Round about on the outside wall of the town were perched marvellous, large, foreign birds from far away, with beaks eager for spoil and claws expectantly crooked; there they sat and looked down with their calm, greedy eyes, as if waiting for the whole unfortunate town to be turned into one single carrion-pit.

Eleven weeks had passed since the outbreak of the plague, when the guards in the tower and others who were standing in high places saw a strange procession cross the plains and turn into the streets of the new town, passing between the stones discolored by smoke and the black heaps of ashes. A crowd of people! At least six hundred men and women, old and young, carrying great black crosses and broad red banners which floated like fire and blood over their heads. They sang as they marched forward, and the mournful tones of utter despair rose through the still, sultry air. (Jens Peter Jacobsen, "The Plague at Bergamo")

Your comments on point of view and voice: _____

_____

_____

_____

_____

A man stood upon a railroad bridge in northern Alabama, looking down into the swift water twenty feet below. The man's hands were behind his back, the wrists bound with a cord. A rope closely encircled his neck. It was attached to a stout cross-timber above his head and the slack fell to the level of his knees. Some loose boards laid upon the sleepers supporting the metals of the railway supplied a footing for him and his executioners— two private soldiers of the Federal Army, directed by a sergeant who in civil life may have been a deputy sheriff. At a short remove upon the same temporary platform was an officer in the uniform of his rank, armed. He was a captain. A sentinel at each end of the bridge stood with his rifle in the position known as "support," that is to say, vertical in front of the left shoulder, the hammer resting on the forearm thrown straight across the chest—a formal and unnatural position, enforcing an erect carriage of the body. It did not appear to be the duty of these two men to know what was occurring at the centre of the bridge; they merely blockaded the two ends of the foot planking that traversed it. (Ambrose Bierce, "An Occurrence at Owl Creek Bridge")

Your comments on point of view and voice: _____

_____

_____

_____

_____

Your comparison of the three authors' use of point of view and voice in

these selections: _____

_____

_____

_____

_____

_____

_____

Exercise 2

To see how point of view influences a story, consider how some stories could be told from a different or unusual point of view. Write a paragraph or two from the point of view suggested for these topics.

1. Describe a play in a football game from the point of view of the goal post.

   _____

   _____

   _____

   _____

   _____

2. Describe a rainstorm from the point of view of an ant.

   _____

   _____

   _____

   _____

   _____

3. Retell part of the story of Red Riding Hood from the point of view of the wolf.

   _____

   _____

   _____

   _____

_____

_____

4. Describe a home run from the point of view of the ball.

_____

_____

_____

_____

5. Using the omniscient narrator's point of view, describe a scene in which two shy teenagers are talking to each other but are unable to communicate the fact that each one likes the other very much.

_____

_____

_____

_____

_____

_____

Exercise 3

Compare the points of view used by Mario Pei, Peter Peregrine, and James Thurber in the stories included at the end of this chapter. If the point of view in each story were different, how would this affect each of the stories?

_____

_____

_____

_____

_____

_____

_____

_____

THE LITERARY PAPER

1. In improvisational comedy, a group on stage is given suggestions by the audience for a skit, usually suggestions for one or more main characters, some elements of the plot or theme, and perhaps even a conclusion. The challenge is to quickly come up with a clever skit, embodying all of the suggested elements. To try this kind of improvisation, form a small group with several other writers and challenge another group by giving them several key elements such as a few characters, a portion of the plot, a situation, and so on. The resulting story need not be humorous. They, in turn, can give your group some suggestions for an improvised story. Exchange suggestions and work with your group to formulate a story that incorporates the elements you have been given.

Suggestions for another group to use in improvising: _____

_____

_____

_____

Suggestions given to your group: _____

_____

_____

_____

_____

_____

Notes for your group's story: _____

_____

_____

_____

_____

_____

_____

_____

_____

2. Have a friend tell a story orally. Note all the elements—situation, character, plot, dramatic conflict, and so on—that were included in the story as your friend told it.

_____

_____

_____

_____

_____

_____

3. For one of the selections at the end of this chapter, write a technical analysis of the methods used to achieve the story's effects. That is, examine how the writer uses plot, character, situation, irony, point of view, symbolism, and so forth.

_____

_____

_____

_____

_____

_____

_____

4. Choose one of the short stories at the end of the chapter and write a brief interpretation of it. Use examples from the story to show how you arrived at your conclusion.

_____

_____

_____

_____

_____

_____

_____

_____

5. Select one of the stories at the end of the chapter or one of the impro-
visations from question 1 above and evaluate it by commenting on the
effectiveness of some important element such as character, plot, or
theme.

_____

_____

_____

_____

_____

_____

_____

_____

WITH HIS ARM IN A SLING

Mario Pei

Tommy Trent from Tuscaloosa crouched in the mud, nervously fingering
his tommy-gun and eyeing the Landsturm trooper who loomed before him.

This was his first real view of the enemy. He had seen a few prisoners
since landing in France, but they were too bedraggled and dejected to be
accounted as real foes. Besides, they were unarmed.

The man before him had a gun. He could see the right hand clutching
the muzzle just below the spike-like bayonet. But what held Tommy fas-
cinated was the German sentry's left hand. Together with the arm, it rested
comfortably in a sling that came down from his neck. Were the Krauts so
hard up for man-power that they had to use one-armed men for sentry
duty? And elderly men at that!

He could see the profile of the Kraut's face beneath the shadow of the coal-scuttle helmet. A bearded face, with a straight, prominent nose and jaw. Not so different, come to think of it, from the face of Tommy's dad, back in Tuscaloosa.

Which started off a train of memories and thoughts in Tommy's head. He remembered the day, about two years back, when Dad came back from the railroad hospital with his arm in a sling. He had broken it on the job. For six weeks he had carried his arm in that sling.

Tommy came to with a start. He thought (but it was only his imagination) that he had heard the beginning of the shrill of Ole Sarge's whistle—the signal to go ahead and let 'em have it. It wasn't. The men hadn't all gotten into position yet, he guessed.

Ole Sarge—now there was a tough old bird. "Hit 'em first and talk to 'em later!" was the motto he was always drilling into the youngsters. "A good Kraut is a dead Kraut!" was the way he explained it. "I fought the so-and-sos in the last war, an' I know what I'm talkin' about!"

"Hit 'em first!" As soon as he'd hear that whistle, he'd be hitting his own particular man, this oldish guy with a profile and beard like dad's and his arm in a sling. "And shoot to kill!" was Ole Sarge's further admonition. "Aim for their bellies! A wounded Kraut can get back at you. A dead one cain't!" Sort of disgusting stuff for a kid just out of high school.

Shucks! Of course he wasn't going to get sentimental about this war. He had seen a couple of buddies knocked off by Kraut shells, and how about Freddy Hoyt, who was walking right beside him when a sniper got him?

Still, it was like kicking a man when he's down. One-armed, taken by surprise, potted without even a chance to say his prayers.

Yeah, war was war! "Get 'em before they get you!" The idea was to get back to Tuscaloosa—and Dad.

So the man looked like Dad when he had his arm in a sling. So what? Tommy's finger tightened on the trigger.

Then the whistle blew, and caught them both by surprise. The Landsturm man stood absolutely motionless while the first shots rang out to the right and left. He wasn't expecting this.

Tommy leaped up from the mud. His tommy-gun was pointed straight at the German's belly. But it didn't go off. Instead, he used one of the phrases he had learned in his language manual. *"Die Hände hoch!"*

The flash came from right inside the sling. It was so near that it burned his sleeve. But the aim of a Luger pistol from inside a sling isn't so good. Good enough, though, to send a burning pain shooting through Tommy's right forearm and make him drop the tommy-gun.

The Luger apparently jammed after that one shot. Tommy Trent stood dazed and paralyzed, not knowing what to do with his good left arm, now that the right dangled helplessly at his side.

The Kraut had thrown aside his rifle. His good right hand reached down to his belt and came out with a wicked trench-knife. One step, one thrust was all he needed to keep Tommy from going back to Tuscaloosa.

He never took that step. Over Tommy's shoulder came the roar of another tommy-gun, and the man who looked like Dad dropped in his tracks.

"Hit 'em first and talk to 'em later, like I tole you, you blankety-blank fool!" grunted Ole Sarge.

THE GODFATHER AND HIS GODCHILD

James Thurber

A worldly-wise collector, who had trotted the globe collecting everything he could shoot, or buy, or make off with, called upon his godchild, a little girl of five, after a year of collecting in various countries of the world.

"I want to give you three things," he said. "Any three things your heart desires. I have diamonds from Africa, and a rhinoceros horn, scarabs from Egypt, emeralds from Guatemala, chessmen of ivory and gold, mooses' antlers, signal drums, ceremonial gongs, temple bells, and three rare and remarkable dolls. Now tell me," he concluded, patting the little girl on the head, "what do you want more than anything else in the world?"

His little godchild, who was not a hesitater, did not hesitate. "I want to break your glasses and spit on your shoes," she said.

MORAL: *Though statisticians in our time have never kept the score, Man wants a great deal here below and Woman even more.*

THE UNICORN IN THE GARDEN

James Thurber

Once upon a sunny morning a man who sat in a breakfast nook looked up from his scrambled eggs to see a white unicorn with a gold horn quietly cropping the roses in the garden. The man went up to the bedroom where his wife was still asleep and woke her. "There's a unicorn in the garden," he said. "Eating roses." She opened one unfriendly eye and looked at him. "The unicorn is a mythical beast," she said, and turned her back on him. The man walked slowly downstairs and out into the garden. The unicorn was still there; he was now browsing among the tulips. "Here, unicorn," said the man, and he pulled up a lily and gave it to him. The unicorn ate it gravely. With a high heart, because there was a unicorn in his garden, the man went upstairs and roused his wife again. "The unicorn," he said, "ate a lily." His wife sat up in bed and looked at him, coldly. "You are a booby," she said, "and I am going to have you put in the booby-hatch."

The man, who had never liked the words "booby" and "booby-hatch," and who liked them even less on a shining morning when there was a unicorn in the garden, thought for a moment. "We'll see about that," he said. He walked over to the door. "He has a golden horn in the middle of his forehead," he told her. Then he went back to the garden to watch the unicorn; but the unicorn had gone away. The man sat down among the roses and went to sleep.

As soon as the husband had gone out of the house, the wife got up and dressed as fast as she could. She was very excited and there was a gloat in her eye. She telephoned the police and she telephoned a psychiatrist; she told them to hurry to her house and bring a strait-jacket. When the police and the psychiatrist arrived they sat down in chairs and looked at her, with great interest. "My husband," she said, "saw a unicorn this morning." The police looked at the psychiatrist and the psychiatrist looked at the police. "He told me it ate a lily," she said. The psychiatrist looked at the police and the police looked at the psychiatrist. "He told me it had a golden horn in the middle of its forehead," she said. At a solemn signal from the psychiatrist, the police leaped from their chairs and seized the wife. They had a hard time subduing her, for she put up a terrific struggle, but they finally subdued her. Just as they got her into the strait-jacket, the husband came back into the house.

"Did you tell your wife you saw a unicorn?" asked the police. "Of course not," said the husband. "The unicorn is a mythical beast." "That's all I wanted to know," said the psychiatrist. "Take her away. I'm sorry, sir, but your wife is as crazy as a jay bird." So they took her away, cursing and screaming, and shut her up in an institution. The husband lived happily ever after.

MORAL: *Don't count your boobies until they are hatched.*

THE RUNAWAY

Peter Peregrine

The little boy crawled out of bed and pulled his shoes and socks on. He was already dressed, and as he went to get his coat he passed an open window and stopped to peer through the flapping curtains at the moonlit forest outside. The wind was blowing the trees wildly, and a light mist hung on the treetops.

The stairs creaked as he walked down them, and he grimaced at the noise. The living room was softly lit by lines of moonlight streaming through the frail curtains. The little boy walked through the room and unlocked the front door. He felt the cold night air rush into the house as he opened the door, and took one last look into the moonlit house before closing it.

Shadows played across the front lawn and the wind blew leaves across the grass. The little boy stood on the front porch for a moment looking at the yard and the forest beyond, both distorted and confused by the swirling light and darkness, and then, taking a deep breath, walked down the front steps, through the yard, and into the woods.

The boy found a path that he knew, and began to follow it through the woods. Moonlight lit the path unevenly as it streamed through the swaying treetops, and the boy went along the path hopping from one pool of light to another. An owl screeched far off in the woods; the boy could barely hear it over the noise of the wind, but as he stopped and listened, he became aware of many noises coming from deep within the forest. A branch broke off a tree and fell on the boy. He ran forward a few steps, and turned to look at where the branch had fallen on him. He looked around him at the surrounding woods, and finding a large tree nearby, curled up under it, and fell slowly into a restless sleep.

As the dawn came, he awoke and started walking again. The path soon shrank to a trickle of brown running through the mountainous trees. The forest where the boy now walked was strange to him. It was thick and full of deep ravines and hills. He followed the little path across all of these as if nothing could stop him, jumping across streams and climbing easily up ponderous hillsides.

Now, in the light, the forest was full of tiny creatures. Squirrels raced through the treetops and birds poked around in the mud. An animal had made its home on the path, and the boy stuck a stick and finally his hand down the hole to see what kind of animal lived there. Nothing came out, but as he was leaving the place the boy saw a badger come through the woods and drop down the hole. Farther on he found a few feathers and blood and tiny pieces of grey fur lying in the path. He picked them up and inspected them for a moment, but soon dropped them and continued on.

Just before dark the little path came to an end. The forest fell behind and a large wheat field glowing in the late afternoon sun spread before the boy. He walked out into the waving grain and sat down. The stalks cradled him as he looked at the sky. A drop of rain hit his face, then another, and another. He stood up and looked around for some shelter. Off in the distance was a rotting, sunken farmhouse. He began running towards it.

It was raining hard as he reached the front steps of the old house. The front door was open, and he was wet and cold, so he went inside. There was nothing in the dark old house but broken glass and fallen plaster. The boy went upstairs.

In a tiny front room there was an old, creaky rocker sitting in a small circle of light coming from the window. He went into the room. There was a puddle of water on the floor, and little drips kept adding to the pool in regular intervals. He could hear the rain on the roof above him. He sat down in the rocking chair, stared out the window at the wheat field for a while, and went to sleep.

DOONESBURY

FEIFFER

13
Planning and Writing the Research Paper

The planning and writing of a research paper are often treated separately because writers must learn a great deal about both topics. However, in this practice book planning and writing are combined so that you can use the same material you've gathered while practicing planning skills for the exercises in the writing stage. Because gathering material for a research paper requires a great deal of effort, you may also wish to combine these practice exercises with your preparation of an assigned research paper for this class or for another course. You'll find long lists of topics, questions, and suggestions if you need help in choosing a subject.

UNDERSTANDING THE ASSIGNMENT

Exercise 1

Some writers prefer to practice their research paper skills on a short paper before plunging into a longer one. Included here is an exercise that can be done as a short (three- to five-page) paper. To do so, select one of the following options.

1. Select a person about whom you think a worthwhile newspaper column could be written for your local paper. The person might be a well-known figure in local government, in your college or university, or in business. Or, the person might be a national or international sports star, political or religious leader, or entertainer. Assume that some of your readers will not know whatever person you choose, some will know the person fairly well, and some will merely recognize the name and little else. As you gather information, attempt to interview the person if at all possible, or talk with others who know your subject; you should also try to find some published material about the person.

    Like any feature story or article, your column must have a thesis and a purpose. Use the title or headline to indicate the focus of the story and the newspaper for which the story is intended.

2. Choose a movie that has been widely shown around the United States or has at least had enough publicity so that there are reviews of it in print. Using three different reference guides in the library, find three reviews of the movie and then write a brief paper summing up the different reviewers' comments on specific aspects of the picture such as plot, acting, directing, and special effects. Include a few quotations from the reviewers' articles also. At the end of your paper list the reference guides you consulted and the movie reviews you read. Follow MLA style.

3. Assume that you are about to write a brief report on a major problem in your college, town, or region. Determine who your audience will be. For example, you might be making a report to the college administration on the recently upgraded facilities for women's sports or reporting to the town or city council on a proposal to reroute traffic away from some overly congested streets. Or you might be reporting to a local welfare agency about the need for services among a group they have not adequately helped. At the end of your report include a list of the people you have interviewed and your other sources of information. Use either MLA or APA style.

Exercise 2

To become familiar with the kinds of research papers that are written in college, interview three teachers on your campus and ask them about the papers they assign. They may be willing to give you copies of written assignments that they distribute in class, or they may describe typical research paper assignments in their field. Find examples from three different fields of study and describe each in a few sentences, noting how long the paper should be, the length of time allowed for its completion, and other requirements. Also, indicate whether the papers are intended to be surveys, arguments, or a combination of both.

1. Academic field: _____

   Description of the assignment: _____

   _____

   _____

   _____

2. Academic field: _____

   Description of the assignment: _____

   _____

   _____

   _____

3. Academic field: _____

   Description of the assignment: _____

   _____

   _____

   _____

Exercise 3

Listed below are some possible subjects for research papers. Drawing on
your general knowledge, summarize in a few sentences some of the issues
or debatable viewpoints for each item in the space provided. What aspects
might you argue for or against if you were to write a research paper on this
subject?

1. The needs of senior citizens in our society

   _____

   _____

   _____

   _____

2. Tobacco growers' influence on cigarette advertising and public smoking
   regulations

   _____

   _____

_____

_____

3. Raising the age for drivers' licenses

_____

_____

_____

4. The relationship between violence in movies and on TV and crime rates

_____

_____

_____

5. The need to improve public schools in America

_____

_____

_____

_____

SELECTING A SUBJECT

Exercise 1

Listed here are suggestions for subjects for a ten- to twelve-page research paper, to be completed in six to eight weeks. In order to evaluate them as possibilities, consider whether or not they might be too autobiographical, too subjective, too restricted, too current, or possibly too specialized for a general audience. Consider also the time available, the length of the paper,

and the possible audience appeal. After considering these criteria, offer a
two- or three-sentence evaluation of each subject in the space provided and
explain the basis for your explanation.

1. The history of puppetry

_____

_____

_____

2. The problems of newly arrived immigrants in your area

_____

_____

_____

3. The tallest building in this state

_____

_____

_____

4. The national craze for customized cars

_____

_____

_____

5. The usefulness of horoscopes

_____

_____

_____

_____

6. Leading causes of mental illness among the rich

_____

_____

_____

7. The national problem of deteriorating highways and bridges

_____

_____

_____

8. Photography as a money-making hobby

_____

_____

_____

9. The medical value of herbal and other folk remedies

_____

_____

_____

Exercise 2

The subjects listed below are too broad and need to be restricted so that they can be treated in a ten- to twelve-page paper. If possible, work with several other writers. Select five of these broad subjects and think of three more restricted subjects for each of them.

General subject	More restricted subjects
World War II	a. _____
	b. _____
	c. _____
computers	a. _____
	b. _____
	c. _____
inflation	a. _____
	b. _____
	c. _____
cancer	a. _____
	b. _____
	c. _____
Indian culture	a. _____
	b. _____
	c. _____
nutrition	a. _____
	b. _____
	c. _____

General subject	More restricted subjects
child care	a. _____
	b. _____
	c. _____
prison reform	a. _____
	b. _____
	c. _____
horse racing	a. _____
	b. _____
	c. _____
ancient Greek drama	a. _____
	b. _____
	c. _____
communicable diseases	a. _____
	b. _____
	c. _____
advertising	a. _____
	b. _____
	c. _____
deserts	a. _____
	b. _____
	c. _____

Exercise 3

Listed here are some additional suggestions for research paper subjects. Look through this list and select or modify one that interests you. Then, explore in writing what you know about the subject or what you'd like to find out about it.

Suggested subjects:

the orphan drug problem
children's literature
the Watergate scandal and its aftereffects
health care for the poor
genetic engineering
sleep research
the day you were born
the use of agent orange in Vietnam
causes and treatments of autism
religious cults
a historical event such as the assassination of John F. Kennedy
vocational education
subliminal advertising
government regulation of the automobile industry
drug abuse
a famous person you'd like to know more about, such as Jesse Jackson, John McEnroe, Paul Cezanne, Stephen Spielberg, Lee Iacocca, Placido Domingo, or Theodore Roosevelt
divorce
the value of preschool education
the aftermath of busing
military defense
earthquakes
imported cars
antiques
the problem of nuclear waste disposal
adoption
the significance of a religious ceremony, such as baptism or the bar mitzvah
a disappearing or little known craft such as blacksmithing, tomb stone engraving, or paper making
a new product or service, such as computerized information networks
solar energy
changing trends in weddings
photojournalism
explorers who have reached the South Pole

the state of American railroads
the paperback industry
the training and use of animals for military purposes
the origin of the Farm Bureau
new developments in the U.S. Postal Service
overcrowded national parks
the problem of drunk drivers
the European or American fashion industry
women's sports
a recent issue confronting the Environmental Protection Agency
the economic health of American symphony orchestras
an unusual or famous museum
black musicians
computerized dating services
legislation to assist the handicapped
college athletics
the problems and successes of a particular ethnic or minority group in
   America

your choice: _____

Subject choice: _____

Your initial reactions and thoughts about this subject: _____

_____

_____

_____

_____

_____

_____

FINDING AND EVALUATING SOURCES

Exercise 1

In order to become familiar with the library you'll be using for your research paper, tour the library's facilities and answer the following questions:

1. What do the following terms mean?

   a. journal: _____

   b. bound valume of journals: _____

   _____

   c. serial: _____

   d. magazine: _____

   e. monograph: _____

   f. bibliography: _____

   g. index: _____

   h. abstract: _____

   i. Library of Congress: _____

   j. call number: _____

   k. card catalog: _____

   l. microfiche: _____

   m. stacks: _____

2. What is the *Readers' Guide to Periodical Literature,* and where is it

   located? _____

   _____

   Does your library have any other similar index? If so, what is the

   title? _____

3. Where is the card catalog located? _____

   _____

4. How do you find the location of specific periodicals? _____

   _____

5. Where is the general reference collection of the library? How do you find specific titles in this collection? _____

_____

_____

6. What specialized encyclopedias does the library have for music?

_____

_____

7. What Library of Congress subject headings exist for the topic of computers? _____

_____

8. Does your library have the PAIS (Public Affairs Information Service) subject index? If so, what is it and where is it located? _____

_____

_____

9. Where is the closest place you can get a soft drink or some coffee if you are using the *Reader's Guide to Periodical Literature*? _____

_____

_____

10. Does your library have a microfilm or microfiche system? If so, where is it located and how do you use it? _____

_____

_____

11. What indexes to newspapers does your library have? _____

_____

_____

12. Where are government documents and publications located? _____

_____

_____

Exercise 2

For each of the following subjects, list five useful sources in your library other than general encyclopedias. Include titles of books and articles, specialized encyclopedias, and indexes.

1. John Updike

    a. _____

    b. _____

    c. _____

    d. _____

    e. _____

2. the recent war between England and Argentina over the Falkland Islands

    a. _____

    b. _____

    c. _____

    d. _____

    e. _____

3. college scholarships

    a. _____

    b. _____

    c. _____

d. _____

e. _____

4. the sinking of the *Titanic*

   a. _____

   b. _____

   c. _____

   d. _____

   e. _____

5. the Boston Tea Party

   a. _____

   b. _____

   c. _____

   d. _____

   e. _____

6. the Sinai Desert

   a. _____

   b. _____

   c. _____

   d. _____

   e. _____

7. the music of George Gershwin

   a. _____

   b. _____

c. _____

d. _____

e. _____

8. Oriental philosophy

    a. _____

    b. _____

    c. _____

    d. _____

    e. _____

9. solar eclipses

    a. _____

    b. _____

    c. _____

    d. _____

    e. _____

10. gene splicing

    a. _____

    b. _____

    c. _____

    d. _____

    e. _____

11. how a steam iron works

    a. _____

b. _____

c. _____

d. _____

e. _____

12. the most recent Supreme Court decisions

a. _____

b. _____

c. _____

d. _____

e. _____

Exercise 3

Select three of the following questions and find the answers by using reference books available in your library. Do not use a general encyclopedia. Write both the results of your search and the sources you used in your investigation. If the question has no answer or cannot be answered by any of the references in your library, you can still indicate how you proceeded in your search.

1. Which company is the largest manufacturer of automobiles in the United States?

_____

_____

_____

_____

2. Which English king did Catherine of Braganza marry? What was her native country?

_____

_____

_____

3. How many people were killed in the St. Valentine's Day Massacre?

_____

_____

_____

4. How did Mozart die?

_____

_____

_____

5. In what year was actress Diana Rigg born?

_____

_____

_____

6. What is the true identity of mystery writer Michael Innes?

_____

_____

_____

7. Why are soap operas called "soap operas"?

_____

_____

_____

8. What is the largest cathedral in France?

_____

_____

_____

9. Who invented the corkscrew?

_____

_____

_____

10. What movie won the greatest number of Academy Awards?

_____

_____

_____

_____

_____

_____

_____

Exercise 4

While many reference books lead to information that can be found in the library, some reference books list names, addresses, and phone numbers of people and organizations who can supply information. If your college or local public library contains the references listed below, browse through four of these indexes, describe their contents, and think of a useful question that might be answered by this reference book. If the book has information on your research paper subject, make your question relevant to your research paper.

Many of these books are published every year. Find the most recent edition.

1. *Thomas' Register of American Manufacturers and Thomas Register Catalog File* (New York: Thomas Publishing Co.)

    Description of the contents: _____

    _____

    _____

    A question that could be answered using this source: _____

    _____

    _____

2. *Writer's Market* (Cincinnati: Writer's Digest Books)

    Description of the contents: _____

    _____

    _____

A question that could be answered using this source: _____

_____

_____

3. *Washington Information Directory* (Washington, D.C.: Congressional Quarterly, Inc.)

Description of the contents: _____

_____

_____

A question that could be answered using this source: _____

_____

_____

4. *U.S. Industrial Directory* (Stamford, Ct.: Cahners)

Description of the contents: _____

_____

_____

A question that could be answered using this source: _____

_____

_____

5. *The U.S. Government Manual* (Washington, D.C.: Office of the Federal Register, National Archives and Records Service, General Service Administration)

Description of the contents: _____

_____

_____

A question that could be answered using this source: _____

_____

_____

6. *Encyclopedia of Associations* (Detroit: Gale Research)

Description of the contents: _____

_____

_____

A question that could be answered using this source: _____

_____

_____

7. *Federal Regulatory Directory* (Washington, D.C.: Congressional Quarterly, Inc.)

Description of the contents: _____

_____

_____

A question that could be answered using this source: _____

_____

_____

Exercise 5

Write a letter requesting an answer to one of the questions you formulated in the exercise above. Address the letter to an appropriate organization listed in the reference book that suggested the question.

_____

_____

_____

_____

_____

_____

_____

_____

_____

_____

_____

_____

Exercise 6

For the research paper you are working on, create a working bibliography
of at least four books and four articles.

_____

_____

_____

_____

_____

_____

_____

_____

_____

_____

_____

_____

_____

_____

In the space provided here, copy an author card for any one of the books you have listed above. In the margins around the card, draw lines to various points of the card and explain the information given.

TAKING NOTES

Included here are some excerpts from longer articles. To practice writing note cards, write three note cards for each excerpt. On one card copy a quotation that you might use if you were writing about this topic. On the second card summarize the principal points in the argument, and on the third card paraphrase, or restate in your own words, some information that you might use in a research paper.

ORIENTEERING: A SPORT WITH DIRECTION

You're standing in the middle of a wooded grove far from any road or house. There's a compass in your left hand and a detailed map in your right. A series of checkpoints is marked on the map, and you estimate that the next one is about a half mile away. But a group of concentric contour lines drawn in brown tells you there is a steep hill between you and your goal. The route over the hill would be shorter, but would it be faster? Would it be better to save time by climbing now, while the legs are still fresh? Or should you go around the hill, following the stream marked in blue on the map? And is it wiser to cross the stream now or later?

This is orienteering, a mixture of marathon, hike, and scavenger hunt, a cross-country race in which participants must locate a series of markers set in unfamiliar terrain by means of map and compass. . . .

The navigational skills involved make orienteering a sport that is challenging to the brain as well as the body. While the growing ranks of American orienteers are filled with long-distance runners and nature lovers attracted by the chance to develop pathfinding skills, the sport also seems to attract problem solvers, people with analytical bent. Many orienteers are engineers, computer programmers, and lawyers. "Orienteering is 50 percent muscle and 50 percent mind," says Robert Defer, director of the United States Orienteering Federation, which coordinates national meets. "It doesn't matter how fast you go if you're moving in the wrong direction."

To navigate, most orienteers use an ordinary plastic compass, the purpose of which is to align the map with the surrounding terrain. The orienteer then uses his wits to compare the map with what he sees. One technique is to look for "handrails," features such as a stream or the edge of a forest that lie in the same direction as the next control point. While sprinting along handrails, orienteers also look for objects such as houses and boulders—which appear on the map—to gauge how far they have traveled. Some even count paces to estimate the distance covered. (Linton Robinson, "Orienteering," *Science 82*)

Note card with a quotation

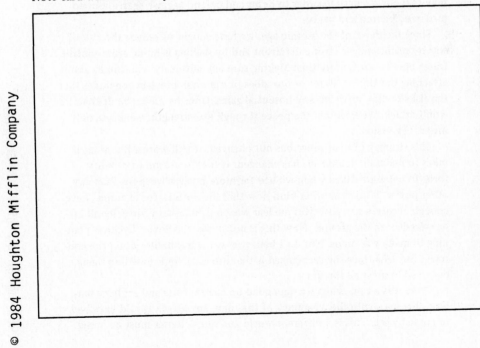

Note card with a summary

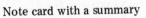

Note card with a paraphrase

```

```

The defense policy of the United States is based on a simple premise: The United States does not start fights. We will never be an agressor. We maintain our strength in order to deter and defend against aggression—to preserve freedom and peace.

Since the dawn of the atomic age, we have sought to reduce the risk of war by maintaining a strong deterrent and by seeking genuine arms control. Deterrence means simply this: Making sure any adversary who thinks about attacking the United States or our allies or our vital interests concludes that the risks to him outweigh any potential gains. Once he understands that, he won't attack. We maintain the peace through our strength; weakness only invites aggression.

This strategy of deterrence has not changed. It still works. But what it takes to maintain deterrence has changed. It took one kind of military force to deter an attack when we had far more nuclear weapons than any other power; it takes another kind now that the Soviets, for example, have enough accurate and powerful nuclear weapons to destroy virtually all of our missiles on the ground. Now this is not to say the Soviet Union is planning to make war on us. Nor do I believe a war is inevitable—quite the contrary. But what must be recognized is that our security is based on being prepared to meet all threats.

There was a time when we depended on coastal forts and artillery batteries because, with the weaponry of that day, any attack would have had to come by sea. This is a different world and our defenses must be based on recognition and awareness of the weaponry possessed by other nations in the nuclear age. (Ronald Reagan, "Peace and National Security," *Vital Speeches*)

Note card with a quotation

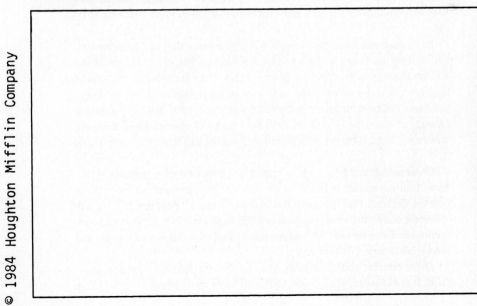

Note card with a summary

Note card with a paraphrase

```
┌──────────────────────────────────────────────────────────────┐
│                                                                │
│                                                                │
│                                                                │
│                                                                │
│                                                                │
│                                                                │
│                                                                │
│                                                                │
│                                                                │
│                                                                │
│                                                                │
│                                                                │
│                                                                │
└──────────────────────────────────────────────────────────────┘
```

If the millions of pounds lost on diets stayed lost, Americans wouldn't be spending billions of dollars each year on diet books, low-calorie foods, and weight loss drugs. Even those dedicated dieters who turn to weight loss clinics for help find their fat hard to part with. For example, studies show that only about five percent can expect to lose 20 pounds and keep them off.

Diets may not work, but people want to believe they do. Like any ritual, dieting has found a myth to give it meaning. The central tenet of the diet mythology is that thin people are *better* than fat ones—more beautiful, healthier, stronger of will. The only way to make this invidious attitude palatable has been to argue that virtually anybody can, with a reasonable amount of conscious effort, control how fat he or she becomes. But with rare exceptions, dieters lose weight temporarily and then gradually regain it.

Common ideas about weight control are based on three assumptions. First, that overeating is the key behavior; fat people must eat more than normal. Second, that the body doesn't really "care" how much fat it has; it merely stores the energy leftovers from each meal. Third, that the conscious mind can be used to balance intake and expenditure of energy and thus achieve any desired weight.

These familiar and apparently obvious assumptions are now proving false. It is not true, for example, that a fat body must belong to a big eater.

To find out just how much people of different sizes eat, psychiatrist Albert Stunkard and his colleagues observed patrons of fast-food restaurants, snack bars, and ice-cream parlors, places where portions are so standardized that it is relatively easy to calculate the number of calories on any tray that is served. The observers were, to be sure, watching people eat only one of their day's meals and that one in public, where obviously piggy behavior might be embarrassing. But the anonymity of the setting should have been sufficient protection for anyone who wanted two or three hamburgers instead of one. When the observers' sheets were tallied, Stunkard found that the fat customers (those judged to be 30 percent overweight) had eaten no more than the thinner ones. Stunkard's finding is the rule rather than the exception; other studies have also shown that fat people eat normal quantities of food and, in some cases, even slightly less. . . .

An alternative theory holds that fatness is not an accident, that the body does "care" about its fat stores. According to this view, now popular among psychologists, there is a control system built into every person dictating how much fat he or she should carry—a kind of thermostat for body fat. And like a thermostat set to maintain a certain temperature, the body's control system has its own *setpoint* for fat. Some individuals have a high setting; others have a low one. The difference is not between the weak and the strong, or between the impulsive and the abstemious. According to this theory, it is a matter of internal controls that are set differently in different people. (William Bennett and Joel Gurin, "Do Diets Really Work?" *Science 82*)

Note card with a quotation

Note card with a summary

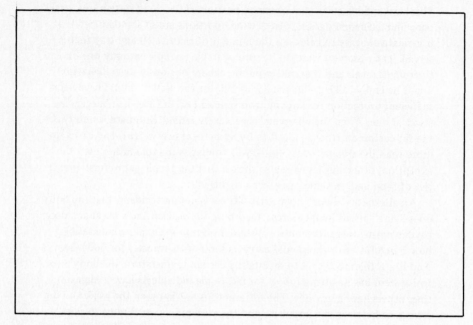

Note card with a paraphrase

Exercise 2

Using the quotations that you have copied from each of the essays, write a sentence or two that might be part of a paper on the subject. Use all or part of the quotation on the card.

1. _____

_____

_____

_____

_____

_____

_____

2. _____

_____

_____

_____

_____

_____

_____

3. _____

_____

_____

_____

_____

_____

_____

_____

_____

ORGANIZING AN OUTLINE

Exercise 1

Included here are preliminary outlines for two student research papers. If possible, look over the outlines with several other writers to see how they might be improved. In each case, consider whether the material is organized in the most effective pattern, whether it seems to cover the subject adequately, whether the major headings are appropriate and useful, and whether some rearranging might be more effective. After considering the outline, write the author a short note indicating the strengths and weaknesses of the outline and some suggestions for revising, if needed.

TELEVISION "COP" SHOWS

Thesis: While "cop" shows have many characteristics that are tied to their particular type of plot development, these same elements also appeal to the general human desire for action, escapism, and heroic deeds.

I. Introduction to "cop" shows
   A. Included in "cop" shows are the private detectives and other crime solvers.
   B. Westerns gave way in popularity to "cop" shows.
   C. Some examples of popular "cop" shows.
II. Characteristics of "cop" shows that are tied to the plot development of crime stories
   A. One or more murders are included in every episode.
   B. The cop is always a nice guy who solves the crime by being smarter and stronger than the criminal.

C. Chase scenes, in cars, planes, helicopters, etc., are usually included.
D. The cop always wins out over the criminal.
E. The endings are short explanations or light jokes.
F. Male cops are usually very attractive to females, and female cops are good looking and well dressed.
III. "Cop" show elements incorporate action, escapism, and heroic deeds
A. Murders and chase scenes involve action.
B. The attractiveness of the main characters and the successful endings are escapism.
C. The main characters always perform heroic deeds. (Student writer)

Your comments to the writer: _____

_____

_____

_____

_____

ARE WE PREPARED FOR WAR?

Thesis: The U.S. is not prepared for a war with the USSR.

I. Critical mass
Using Ray S. Cline's theory of critical mass (which involves land area and population), we can see that the U.S. is at a disadvantage in fighting the Soviets.
II. Economic capability
America is superior in overall economic strength because of its industrial production and agriculture, but the USSR is self-sufficient with oil.
III. Military capability
In terms of hardware, the U.S. is inferior to the Soviets in the following: number of missiles, technologically advanced submarines, strategic bombers, and sophistication of the newest missiles.
IV. The people's will
I believe Americans are not ready for another war and wouldn't make the needed sacrifices.

V. Effects of nuclear war
    We will not be able to withstand a Soviet attack even if we are able to retaliate. (Student writer)

Your comments to the writer: _____

_____

_____

_____

_____

_____

Exercise 2

Make a preliminary outline for your research paper. If possible, share it with the same group of writers with whom you evaluated the research paper outlines in the preceding exercises. Using the same criteria, ask them to comment on the strengths and weaknesses of your outline and to suggest revisions, if needed.

Readers' comments on your outline: _____

_____

_____

_____

_____

_____

_____

_____

WRITING THE FIRST DRAFT

Exercise 1

Included here are the introductions to first drafts of two student research papers. If possible, form a small group with several other writers and evaluate these introductions by answering the revision questions included after each excerpt.

TELEVISION AND SPORTS KICKOFF TO AN UNENDING SEASON

The interaction between sports and television has come to be a prominent issue in our society. "It has come to be an apparent love match between TV and sports that is really a marriage of convenience."[1] Television increases tremendously the amount of money teams and individuals receive and at the same time creates new fans. Sports, in turn, gives TV an endless amount of entertainment. "Turn on the camera, follow the ball, and there it is—instant trauma and excitement. Who will win? How will they manage it? Stay tuned and see."[2] This interaction between sports and television has created a phenomenal amount of money, endless hours of sports on television, and a broadcaster's circus. It is truly a "marriage of convenience."

"TV money has transformed professional athletes from somewhat scruffy mercenaries playing children's games to respected members of the community."[3] This is especially true for football players because in the past they had been thought of as big, dumb guys out playing a stupid game. But now how can society think of them in that respect when television has transformed them into celebrities and their income makes a large part of them millionaires. TV has made these sports stars richer and more famous than ever. Chris Evert Lloyd, Jack Nicklaus, and O. J. Simpson and many other more recent stars make as much or more from advertisement endorsements and other outside interests as they do from playing games. TV is smart in using these sports superstars in other activities such as commercials because it attracts our interest to the product they are advertising. This works to everyone's benefit because the advertiser has a successful campaign and the sports star receives good money. So, in the mingle between advertisers and sports stars, it seems that they each get what they want and help each other in the process.

This is even more apparent when we look back at sports before television. Athletes were by no means as successful in terms of wealth. And, even after television and athletes joined forces, their connection was not immediately a prosperous one. "When the Detroit Lions played the N.Y. Giants in the 1935 NFL championship game, each player on the winning team received

$174. In the 1977 Super Bowl each of the victorious Oakland Raiders got $15,000. The losing Minnesota Vikings consoled themselves with $7,500 each. As one can see that is a big difference."[4] More recently, the difference is even more dramatic. It is estimated that each of the National League teams receives more than $82 million annually from television.[5] What has made this great difference? It required several ingredients to move a somewhat tenuous attraction between television and sports into a mutually beneficial relationship. First, network programmers had to be convinced that sports could be aired on prime time. Then, the rivalry between networks and advertisers added the necessary inflation of sports into major events, and finally, when producers transformed mere "telecasts" into entertainment by adding their show biz touch, sports made it into the inner ring of success. (Student writer)

1. Judging from the introductory paragraphs, what is the writer trying to do in this draft? _____

   _____

   _____

   _____

2. What are the strengths and weaknesses of these opening paragraphs?

   _____

   _____

   _____

   _____

3. What revisions would you recommend for the next draft?

   _____

   _____

   _____

   _____

THE PRESS AND ITS SOURCES

The press is a very important part of our government because it acts as a sort of fourth branch to help shape and reveal public opinion to the decision makers in government. The press also helps to create a dialog among those interested in the issues of the day and also acts to inform the public of the views of their elected public officials. Consequently, the press is an important part of our society, but it is also a powerful part simply because of its role. It can exert or relieve pressure on certain issues, policies, or persons by its content, and because it can, it must be used wisely.

Like any agency of power, the press has its problems. One issue involving the press stands out though. This issue involves the credibility of the information which the press publishes to inform us of what's going on in Washington. The problem here doesn't lie in the press itself, but with its sources. Since the press relies heavily upon outside sources for much of its information, it becomes dependent upon their credibility and motives. Consequently, it is the reader who must be aware of this problem and remember to ask what the motives are of the people revealing the information.

In the U.S. today hundreds of policy decisions are made each day by each level of our government, from city and county to state and national agencies and legislatures. Each of these decisions is supposedly made in light of public opinion so as to be a representation of the public's will. But how do public officials gain access to public opinion and how do they voice their opinions? The basic means of communication used to accomplish this task is the press. As Delmer D. Dunn sees it, "The press goes about this task in four ways: 1) by focusing attention on a subject, 2) by meeting the information needs of public officials, 3) by informing the public of the views of public officials, and 4) by acting as an indicator of the success of the official's activities."[1]

Each day hundreds of newspapers, radio, and TV stations report the news "as they see it." "As they see it" means as they report it or as they decide to focus the eye of America that day. The press has the ability to focus attention on any subject at any moment. Whether it's a crisis in the Middle East, payoffs in Washington, fighting in South America, or a lost rhino in Los Angeles, it can all be brought to public attention through a news story. When the press decides to focus attention on an issue, it immediately begins to take part in the decision-making processes of this country. (Student writer)

1. Judging from the introductory paragraphs, what is the writer trying to

do in this draft? _____

_____

_____

_____

_____

2. What are the strengths and weaknesses of these opening paragraphs?

_____

_____

_____

_____

3. What revisions would you recommend for the next draft? _____

_____

_____

_____

_____

Exercise 2

Read over the first draft of your research paper and answer the revision questions listed below.

1. What were you trying to do in this draft? _____

_____

_____

_____

2. What are the strengths and weaknesses of this draft? _____

_____

_____

_____

3. What revisions are needed in the next draft? _____

_____

_____

_____

    When you have answered these questions, have another writer read your first draft and your answers to the questions. Then, ask the other writer to respond to this question:

What other suggestions can you offer that would improve the next draft?

_____

_____

_____

_____

QUOTING SOURCES

Exercise 1

What are the penalties for plagiarism at your college or university?

_____

_____

_____

_____

_____

Exercise 2

Paraphrase the excerpts in Exercise 1 under "Taking Notes," above. Also, paraphrase an excerpt from one of your sources for your research paper. Clip a copy of your excerpt here.

1. _____

   _____

   _____

   _____

   _____

   _____

   _____

   _____

2. _____

   _____

   _____

   _____

   _____

   _____

3. _____

   _____

   _____

DOCUMENTING SOURCES

Exercise 1

Included here are some exercises to practice using accepted formats for listing sources.

1. In Morton M. Hunt's book, *The World of the Formerly Married*, which was published in New York in 1966 by McGraw-Hill Book Company, he says the following on page 93: "If, in addition, there are children of the marriage, the parents have (in cold blood, anger, or desperation) decided to destroy their prospect of a permanent home."
    a. Assume that you are writing a paper on the effects of divorce on children. Use MLA style and include this quotation in a sentence that might appear in the paper and write the appropriate footnote. Assume that this would be the ninth footnote in your paper.

    The sentence using the quotation:

    _____

    _____

    _____

    _____

    The footnote:

    _____

    _____

    _____

    b. Write the bibliographical entry that would appear at the end of your paper in MLA style.

    _____

    _____

    _____

c. Assume that you've been asked to switch to APA style and that you want to paraphrase Mr. Hunt's comments. Write the sentence as it would appear in a paper.

_____

_____

_____

d. At the end of a paper that includes the sentence you have just written, use APA style for the entry that would be included in the list of sources.

_____

_____

_____

2. In Alexander W. Astin's book entitled *Preventing Students from Dropping Out,* which was published by Jossey-Bass, Inc. in San Francisco, in 1979, Mr. Astin wrote the following: "Dropping out is like the weather, something everyone talks about but no one does anything about." This sentence appeared on page 43 of the book.

a. Assume that you are writing about the problem of student dropouts and want to include this quotation from Mr. Astin's book. Using MLA format, write a sentence containing the quotation and the accompanying footnote, which is the sixth footnote in your paper.

The sentence using the quotation:

_____

_____

_____

The footnote:

_____

_____

_____

b. Write the bibliographical entry for this book in MLA style.

_____

_____

_____

c. Switch to APA style and write the entry that would appear in the list of sources at the end of your paper.

_____

_____

_____

Exercise 2

Rewrite these sources as footnotes and as bibliographical entries in MLA format.

1. In the March 8, 1982, issue of *U.S. News & World Report*, William J. Casey wrote an article entitled "The Real Soviet Threat in El Salvador —and Beyond." The article appeared on pages 23, 24, 25, and 26.

   Footnote entry:

   _____

   _____

   Bibliographical entry:

   _____

   _____

2. In the *Wilmington Globe*, on October 20, 1983, there was an article entitled "Health Care for the Elderly," which was written by J. P. Endicott. It appeared in the first column of the first page of Section B of the newspaper.

Footnote entry:

_____

_____

_____

Bibliographical entry:

_____

_____

_____

3. The U.S. Department of Health and Human Services published a book in 1977 entitled *Fact Sheet: Autism.* There is no author or other information listed on the book's title page, but on the back of the title page it states that the book was published in Bethesda, Maryland.

Footnote entry:

_____

_____

_____

Bibliographical entry:

_____

_____

_____

4. The book entitled *Democracy for the Few*, written by Michael Parenti, was published by St. Martin's Press, in New York. In 1977 the second edition was published.

Footnote entry:

_____

_____

_____

Bibliographical entry:

_____

_____

5. "My Papa's Waltz" was written by Theodore Roethke and was re-printed, on page 76, in *The Little Brown Reader*, edited by Marcia Stubbs and Sylvan Barnet, in 1980. The book is published by Little, Brown and Company, in Boston.

Footnote entry:

_____

_____

Bibliographical entry:

_____

_____

6. Ernest Tuveson edited a book of Jonathan Swift's essays entitled *Swift: A Collection of Critical Essays*. Prentice-Hall, in Englewood Cliffs, New Jersey, published the book in 1964.

Footnote entry:

_____

_____

Bibliographical entry:

_____

_____

_____

14
Business Writing

PARTS OF A LETTER

Exercise 1

You are planning to write to a former employer to ask for a reference. Set up the parts of the letter by inserting the appropriate information inside each of the blocks. Complete all parts of the letter except for the body.

Return Address and Date

Inside Address

Salutation

(BODY OF THE LETTER)

Complimentary Close and Signature

Exercise 2

Assume that you have a question about a magazine subscription and want to write the publisher. Set up the parts of the letter by filling in the spaces inside the blocks.

Return Address and Date

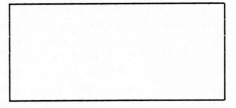

Inside Address

Salutation

(BODY OF THE LETTER)

Complimentary Close and Signature

TYPES OF LETTERS

Letters of Complaint

Exercise 1

In each of these situations do the following:

a. First, write what you'd really like to say in a response. Be as mad, angry, sarcastic, threatening, or negative as you want to be.
b. Then, rewrite the letter in a neutral or positive manner that is more likely to get your message across in a productive way.

Situation 1

About a month ago you bought an expensive pair of Olympia jogging shoes from a local store. Within a few weeks the sole of one of the shoes wore through and actually began to leak. You brought the shoe back to the store where you purchased it, but since you had long since thrown away your purchase receipt, the store owner would not exchange the shoe. Her claim was that without a purchase receipt she had no way of knowing how long you have had the shoes or whether you really bought the shoes in that store. Having paid over $35 for the shoes, you think they should last more than three weeks and that the guarantee in the box should apply in local stores. After all, you have better things to do with your time than write letters to manufacturers. Even if they allow an exchange, you face an extra expense of time and money in shipping the shoes back to them.

Negative letter:

_____

_____

_____

_____

_____

_____

_____

_____

Neutral or positive letter:

_____

_____

_____

_____

_____

_____

_____

_____

Situation 2

When you received an advertisement for a new magazine entitled *Today's World*, there was an offer to send you a free introductory issue of the magazine. The letter also said that if you didn't want to subscribe to the magazine after looking through the first issue, all you had to do was to notify them that you were canceling your subscription. Of course, the letter assured you, you could keep the issue you received, along with the bonus gift of an attractive wall poster. When the complimentary issue of the magazine arrived, it really didn't interest you and you notified the company appropriately in a letter. Three weeks later, a second issue of the magazine arrived and then, a day later, a bill for your subscription. Again, you notified the publisher to cancel your subscription, but you figured that two notifications were enough. Since that time you have received three more issues of the magazine, plus two rather insistent bills. In today's mail was a notice from a collection agency stating that your future credit ratings are in danger because of this unpaid bill. Write to the publisher of the magazine.

Negative letter:

_____

_____

_____

_____

_____

_____

_____

_____

Neutral or positive letter:

_____

_____

_____

_____

_____

_____

_____

Situation 3

On the first day of a large lecture course, students were assigned seats and asked to use only those seats for purposes of attendance records. On the chart posted on the wall you saw that your seat was D-14, and you have been sitting there ever since. Four weeks after the course began, you received a warning notice that your grade will be lowered because of lack of attendance at lectures. Since you have never been absent, this startled you.

When you checked with the teacher, he stated that the attendance logs taken by a teaching assistant for the course showed that you have been consistently absent since the first day. When you noticed that they have you assigned to F-14, you explained that you had seen your seat listed as D-14 and have been sitting there. The teacher has no proof of this and is reluctant to believe your statement. He won't accept the word of other students who have been sitting next to you or even look at your class notes since neither of these constitutes proof as far as he is concerned. To make matters worse, the teaching assistant who took attendance can't remember whether or not she had seen anyone sitting in D-14 (people listening in as auditors are allowed to sit in any vacant seat).

Now you find that the only way to appeal is by a letter to the Dean of Students Office. If the Dean of Students Office accepts your appeal, your teacher will be notified and your "absences" will be erased from your class record.

Negative letter:

_____

_____

_____

_____

_____

_____

_____

Neutral or positive letter:

_____

_____

_____

_____

_____

_____

_____

Exercise 2

You ordered a charcoal-gray wool coat ($165) from S.A. Stevenson Company in Whitman, Maryland 01972. Their representative, Arnold McNeil, took your measurements when he was in town taking orders. Friends highly recommended these tailor-made coats because of their excellent fit and reasonable price. (You saw a similar coat that did not fit as well at a local store for $225.) When Mr. McNeil took your measurements, he said the coat would arrive in approximately a month. Two months from the order date, the coat finally arrives, but the sleeves are an inch too long and the coat should be about two and ½ inches shorter. You have checked with a local tailor who will make the necessary alterations for $15. If the Stevenson Company is willing to send you a check for that amount, you'll keep the coat. If not, you will return it for alterations at their expense. Write a letter of adjustment to the company and keep a neutral or positive tone.

_____

_____

_____

_____

_____

_____

_____

Exercise 3

You have recently rented an apartment that is more expensive than you had planned, but you decided it would be worth it to have a quiet place in which to live. However, having moved in two weeks ago, you find that the walls are like tissue paper and your next-door neighbor's loud stereo is a major distraction. Moreover, because the contract you signed did not ban pets from the building, you brought along Murphy, your kitten. Now, the building manager tells you that pets are forbidden and that you have to get rid of Murphy, even though he is a quiet house cat who never goes outside. The building manager is totally uncooperative about the noise next door and about your pet. Try writing to the company that manages the building to ask what can be done about these problems. The company's name and address are as follows:

Farm Hill Management, Inc.
7200 Graybriar Road West
Chicago, Illinois 61601

Your letter:

_____

_____

_____

_____

_____

_____

_____

Letters of Application

1. Interview two or three people who are in charge of hiring personnel who apply for jobs in their companies by submitting letters of application with accompanying data sheets. Ask the people you are interviewing to describe the characteristics of effective letters and also of letters that are poorly written or likely to be rejected. Record your findings here.
   a. Characteristics of effective letters: _____

   _____

   _____

   _____

   _____

   _____

b. Characteristics of ineffective or poorly written letters: _____

_____

_____

_____

_____

2. Browse through lists of jobs available through your college job placement service or advertised in newspapers, trade journals, or professional journals. Select a job you might apply for, given your qualifications
and interests. First (on a separate sheet of paper) plan, draft, and revise a resume. Then write a letter of application for the job.

_____

_____

_____

_____

_____

_____

3. Look through books listing scholarship awards or through lists of campus jobs, service organizations, or student government positions. Select
one for which you might qualify that requires a written application and
then complete the following planning sheet. Afterwards, write a letter
of application based on your planning sheet.

Planning Sheet

Qualifications asked for: Qualifications that meet these
                                    requirements:

_____   _____

Qualifications asked for: Qualifications that meet these
                                             requirements:

_____   _____

_____   _____

_____   _____

_____   _____

_____   _____

_____   _____

Letter of Application

_____

_____

_____

_____

_____

_____

_____

_____

Letters of Inquiry

If you decide to mail the letters you write for these exercises, you may
want to share with other writers the types of responses you receive.

Select a country that you'd like to travel to or study in for a semester or
two. In preparation for the trip you'll need information about visas, immu-
nizations, customs, and other matters that occur to you. You'd also like
some government travel brochures describing the country, including hotel

listings and maps. Locate the address for the national tourist office for this country in the phone book for a major city, such as New York or Washington, D.C. In the space provided below, plan your questions and then write a letter asking for the information you need. Your college or community library will probably have phone books for major American cities.

Your questions: _____

_____

_____

_____

_____

Your letter: _____

_____

_____

_____

_____

_____

_____

_____

_____

   Choose a company that you might really like to work for and locate their address either through your college placement service or in directories available in the library. If you can, find the name of an appropriate person to write to. What questions about the company would provide information that will help you decide whether or not to work for this company? Make a planning list of the questions first and then write a letter asking those questions.

Your questions: _____

_____

_____

_____

_____

Your letter: _____

_____

_____

_____

_____

_____

_____

Choose a product that you've been considering buying. What information do you want before making an investment in this product? Locate the manufacturer's address either in a directory or on one of their products. Plan your questions and then write your letter.

Your questions: _____

_____

_____

_____

_____

Your letter: _____

_____

_____

_____

_____

_____

_____

   In a local newspaper you have seen an advertisement by a company looking for salespeople to sell their products in your area. You are interested in a possible part-time job, but the ad was vague about several aspects of the job and you'd like more information. For example, you would like to know whether you have to buy the product from them or whether they supply a certain amount and take back unsold merchandise. Also, you'd like to know more about minimum quantities you have to sell, what the profits are, and so on. Select a company whose ad you have seen recently, list the questions you'd want answers to, and write the letter.

Your questions: _____

_____

_____

_____

_____

Your letter: _____

_____

_____

_____

_____

_____

_____

EVALUATING AND REVISING BUSINESS LETTERS

Exercise 1

Each of the sentences below contains one or more problems with negative phrasing, apologetic tone, wordiness, jargon, lack of clarity, lack of specificity, or overemphasis on self-interest rather than reader interest. Identify the major problem(s) in each sentence and then revise it. You may wish to do this exercise in a small group with several other writers.

1. My thorough college training in supervision, my rapid and well-deserved advancement through multitudinous extracurricular activities to leadership positions, and autonomous work experience will enable me to serve you well jobwise as a first-time supervisor.

   Problems in this sentence: _____

   _____

   _____

   _____

   Revised version: _____

   _____

   _____

   _____

   _____

   _____

2. Like all other graduates in Hotel and Restaurant Management from this college, I have taken the usual courses in foods, nutrition, management,

etc., and I didn't do too badly in any of these courses. I haven't yet had much opportunity to gain practical experience outside of my courses, but I hope to learn quickly in my first job.

Problems in these sentences: _____

_____

_____

_____

Revised version: _____

_____

_____

_____

3. Is the Mytaka camera easy to use?

Problems in this sentence: _____

_____

_____

Revised version: _____

_____

_____

4. I thought the shelves would be easy to assemble because I believed the inflated claims on the box; however, I now know the kind of deception your company practices and your total lack of interest in helping the customer to use your product!

Problems in this sentence: _____

_____

_____

Revised version: _____

_____

_____

_____

5. I've had lots of experience in sales, and I am sure I can convince you of my dynamic ability to sell your product.

Problems in this sentence: _____

_____

_____

Revised version: _____

_____

_____

6. I want some information about your product, the Cowahama motorbike, because I may want to consider buying it if I like your answers. Is it expensive? Will it last long? Will I get a decent trade-in when I am ready to sell it?

Problems in these sentences: _____

_____

_____

Revised version: _____

_____

_____

7. I am seeking employment in the construction industry, employment which would afford me the opportunity to obtain my professional registration, to gain experience in all phases of construction, design, estimating, planning, and construction management, and lead to a management responsibility position. A job in your company would help me to obtain my goal.

Problems in these sentences: _____

_____

_____

Revised version: _____

_____

_____

_____

8. In the instance of the latter case, I find that I am unable to obtain con-
sensus from my colleagues as to whether or not your stipulated warran-
ty is applicable in the case described. Your response to this question
will be appreciated as we need to determine whether or not the warran-
ty covers such matters.

Problems in these sentences: _____

_____

_____

Revised version: _____

_____

_____

_____

9. Any added information you can offer beyond answers to my questions
will be appreciated.

Problem in this sentence: _____

_____

_____

Revised version: _____

_____

_____

10. Since I will be graduating in two years, I am now looking for summer employment which will round out my education.

Problem in this sentence: _____

_____

_____

Revised version: _____

_____

_____

11. Because many of my classes were product-oriented, I've had lots of valuable experience in the area of testing products.

Problem in this sentence: _____

_____

_____

Revised version: _____

_____

_____

12. I know that I should have read the instructions more carefully since the answer to the problem is probably there, but maybe you can offer some help too.

Problem in this sentence: _____

_____

_____

Revised version: _____

_____

_____

Exercise 2

Assume that you are Mr. Pirkle, a busy executive who is responsible for selecting candidates for jobs in your department of the Federal Bank of Florida in Fort Lauderdale. Yesterday you received fourteen letters of application for a summer job opening now available, and in this morning's mail another ten letters arrived. Of yesterday's batch about three looked promising; you have held on to them and rejected the others. In today's mail is the letter included here. Read the letter and decide whether you would put it in the group to be considered or in the rejected pile. Indicate the reasons for your decision in the space provided. You may want to work with a small group of other writers in making your decision and in explaining why you made that decision.

490 Smith Hall
Crandall University
West Haverford, MD 23311

Mr. Charles Pirkle
Management Development Specialist
Federal Bank of Florida, Inc.
15 West Church Street, Box 282
Fort Lauderdale, Florida 34101

Dear Mr. Pirkle,

I am interested in summer employment in order to gain advanced experience in my major. In the process of obtaining a management degree from Crandall University, I have studied accounting, industrial relations, and finance. I feel these courses serve as a good beginning into the world of banking and management, but pure education is not enough. Solid experience on how to use the knowledge gained in college is the final step in the making of an effective manager.

I realize in working for a bank, a high level of trust must be maintained. As a bank teller, as shown on the enclosed resume, I have been bonded and thus received that note of trust. From previous experience I have also gained a good background in general banking procedures such as balancing cash drawers and maintaining good customer relations. These already learned skills will cut down on training time and will increase the time I'll spend working for your company.

To enable me to work more effectively with customers and employees, I am specializing in Industrial Relations. As a result of this specialization, I will be able to figure out ways to understand and fulfill the needs of your employees, handle customers with problems, and soothe irate customers.

When you have looked over the enclosed data sheet, which shows more fully my experience and education, please call me to let me know when I may speak to a member of Federal Bank of Florida, Inc. about the possibility of summer employment with your firm.

Respectfully yours,

James Evans

James Evans

enclosure

JAMES EVANS

Present Address:

490 Smith Hall
Crandall University
West Haverford, MD 23311
   phone: 492-330-1718

Permanent Address:

23 Lavell Place
Essex, NH 05418
   phone: 312-216-1927

Objectives

Summer employment in a bank to gain first-hand knowledge and experience in banking, management, and especially industrial relations

Education

B.S. in Management from Crandall University, expected May 1986
Cumulative Grade Index: 5.02/6.0

Major related courses:
   Accounting (I, II), Industrial Relations (I, II, III), Finance, Marketing, Organizational Behavior, Economics

Experience

Bank teller   May–August 1984
                    May–August 1983

Federated Bank, Essex, NH

Prepared daily bank deposits, updated deposit records, cleared and changed registers, made cash transactions with customers

Counselor   May–August 1982
                    May–August 1981
                    May–August 1980

Mount Holly Boy Scout Reservation, Ardan, NH

Instructor for merit badges, daily lifeguard duty, office clerk for camp director, dining hall steward

Honors and Activities

Society for the Advancement of Management
Accounting Club
New Hampshire State Scholarship
College Intramurals (football, hockey)

References

Available upon request

Your decision about this letter:

_____

_____

_____

Reasons for your decision:

_____

_____

_____

_____